Books should be returned on or before the
last date stamped below.

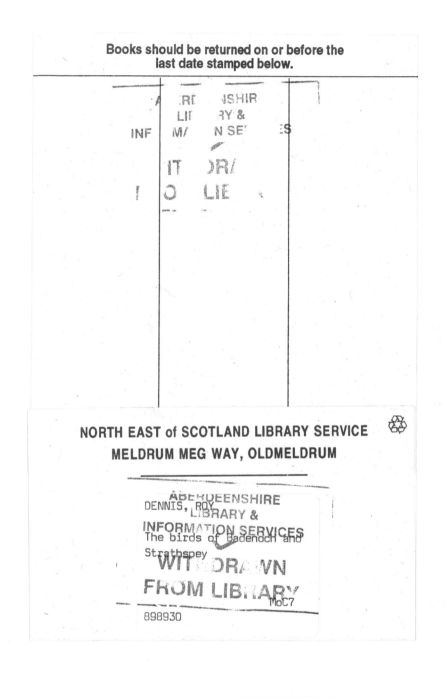

NORTH EAST of SCOTLAND LIBRARY SERVICE
MELDRUM MEG WAY, OLDMELDRUM

The
BIRDS
of Badenoch & Strathspey

Published in Great Britain in 1995 by

Colin Baxter Photography Ltd
Grantown-on-Spey
Scotland PH26 3NA

A CIP catalogue record for this book is available from the British Library

ISBN 0-948661-62-3

Front Cover Photograph: Neil McIntyre
Back Cover Photograph: Colin Baxter

The
BIRDS
of Badenoch & Strathspey

Roy Dennis

Colin Baxter Photography, Grantown-on-Spey, Scotland

Acknowledgments

Firstly I am most grateful to all those bird-watchers and local people who sent me records of birds and told me of additions to my first book of the birds of Badenoch and Strathspey. I am most grateful to the Scottish Ornithologists' Club and their present local recorder, Colin Crooke for the use of records sent in for the annual Highland and Scottish Bird Reports. I am also most grateful to Stewart Taylor and his RSPB colleagues at Abernethy reserve and to Zul Bhatia and his RSPB colleagues at Insh Marshes reserve for access to their bird records. I am indebted to Zul for the use of his updated species lists.

The vignettes, used in the first edition, by Colin Crooke, John Love, Dave Pullan and Richard Richardson have been supplemented with new sketches by Bob Procter. Julie Skinner ably re-typed the original species list and I am indebted to my wife Marina for help with editing and organising this new book on the birds of Badenoch and Strathspey.

MoC7
898930

Contents

THE DISTRICT OF BADENOCH AND STRATHSPEY

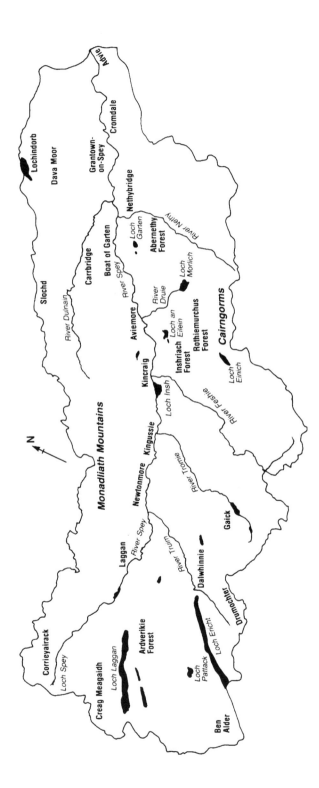

Introduction

Badenoch and Strathspey has always been a special venue for people interested in birds. The combination, within this relatively small area, of the high Cairngorms, the best remnants of the Caledonian Forest and the lovely River Spey, with its associated lochs, means that there is a rich diversity of bird life including many rare species such as crested tit, osprey and capercaillie, as well as Britain's only endemic bird species, the Scottish crossbill.

The mountains surrounding the valley of the Spey contain some of Scotland's highest peaks with an arctic alpine climate, and birds such as dotterel, ptarmigan and golden eagle. The moorlands, so beautiful in late summer with the blooming of the purple heather, are extensive and are home to red deer, red grouse as well as a whole range of other wildlife. The birch wood, croft and farmlands, lochs, rivers, and marshes create a rich mosaic of beautiful countryside where wildlife and people live and work in harmony. The native Scots pine forests, with some trees well over 300 years of age, are true reminders of the ancient Forest of Caledon where long ago moose, brown bear, wolf and wild boar roamed. There is a Scandinavian feel to the landscape and climate which results in this region being one of the best places to see rare breeding birds, such as osprey, goldeneyes and redwings, which have colonised Scotland from Sweden. When I published *Birds of Badenoch & Strathspey* in June 1984, 219 species of birds were listed for the district. The total now stands at 237, although six of them are species which have been released or escaped from captivity, giving a district list of wild birds 231. One hundred and twenty-one species regularly breed here, while a further 31 species have bred once, very spasmodically or no longer do so, although some of them occur regularly as migrants. A further 85 species occur on migration or have been recorded as vagrants. Lesser spotted woodpecker was included in the 1984 list but the records are no longer accepted.

I have known and loved Strathspey and the Cairngorms since 1960, and I hope this guide helps you to explore and enjoy this outstanding area of Scotland. I will be pleased to receive information, past or present, which updates the comments on individual species.

Roy Dennis, April 1995
Inchdryne, Nethy Bridge, Inverness-shire, PH25 3EF Scotland

The District of Badenoch and Strathspey

High in the Monadhliath mountains of the central Highlands of
Scotland, a beautiful river begins a journey of 107 miles to the
North Sea. The river is the Spey. Famous for whisky and salmon, it
flows along a broad strath passing through many communities
including Kingussie, Aviemore and Grantown-on-Spey. To the north
are the Monadhliaths, *monadh* meaning mountain and *liath* is the
gaelic for grey, while to the south are the Cairngorms or Monadh
Ruadhs, the red mountains. This is Badenoch and Strathspey, an
administrative district of a quarter of a million hectares and part of
Highland Region. The district stretches 60 miles from south-west to
north-east and about 20 miles from north to south. It is bordered
by Perthshire in the south, Lochaber in the west, Inverness and
Nairn in the north and Moray, Banff and Aberdeenshire in the east.
The larger centres are Kingussie, Aviemore and Grantown-on-Spey
with about 10,000 people living in the area.

Some people call this area Speyside but that name refers to the
lower reaches of the river around Aberlour and Craigellachie. The
land from the headwaters of the Spey down to Kinrara is known as
Badenoch, while the broader strath from there to Cromdale is called
Strathspey. People have lived in the valley for something like 5,000
years and nowadays the main employment is agriculture, forestry,
tourism, service and light industries and sporting estates.

The altitude of the district ranges from 150 metres (450 feet)
above sea level to 1,235 metres (4,248 feet), so even the low ground
is at a relatively high altitude and well removed from the sea. In
fact, the nearest sea coast is 15 miles away from Lochindorb on the
north-east boundary. The mountains are of granite with areas of
schists and gneisses. There is much evidence of glaciation since this
land was covered in huge ice sheets and glaciers. The Cairngorms
are unique in the British Isles for having the most extensive area of

plateaux over 1,000 metres including four of the five highest mountains in Britain. The Monadhliaths to the north are lower, with rolling hills covered in more acidic moorland and peat hags, while to the west the higher mountains such as Ben Alder and Creag Meagaidh, are grassier and more west coast in character. On the moorlands, heather is the dominant plant giving the hills a beautiful purple hue in late summer, although this predominance by heather is due to the destruction of woodland cover. Lower down some of the very best remnants of the ancient 'Forest of Caledon' are to be found at Rothiemurchus and Abernethy. Alluvial deposits along the river flats provide fertile land for cultivation.

The river Spey rises in the mountains to the west of the Corrieyarrick Pass and flows into the small and remote Loch Spey. It flows rapidly in upper Badenoch but after Kingussie the river is slow running and meanders through the Insh Marshes. In times of heavy rain or snow melt, this low lying land floods. It is a superb area of marshlands and lochs which acts like a gigantic sponge. Badenoch had always been known as the flooded land and although many areas were drained and farmed in the past it has now once more reverted to marshes. The Spey continues its slow journey and passes through some of the best farmland in the district. After Grantown-on-Spey it, once more, becomes a boisterous fast-flowing river tumbling towards the sea at Spey Mouth. Other lovely rivers cascade out of the mountains to join the Spey. Within the district the main ones are the Truim, Tromie, Feshie, Druie and Nethy which flow from Drumochter Pass and the Cairngorms, and the Calder and Dulnain which rise in the Monadhliaths. There is a wealth of beautiful lochs from Lochindorb in the east, with its ancient castle, to Loch Laggan in the west. The high mountain lochs and lochans are often scenic but lacking in wildlife while some of the lower level lochs are excellent for birds.

The climate is distinctly continental because of the distance from the sea. The climate is much wetter in the west while to the east are the dry areas of the Moray Plain. There is a rainfall gradient from west to east but in general the rainfall is about 30–40 inches per year in the valley and at least double that amount in the mountains. Flash floods can occur in late summer while the driest period is usually in the first half of the year. Snowfall is often plentiful and occurs in the mountains on many days between September and April, with fresh snow possible in any month of the year. High winds can cause much drifting of snow and some of the snowfields in the high corries last throughout the whole year. Temperatures can drop down to –20 °C in winter while hard frosts can occur from September to May. Even so, during some winters temperatures are regularly above freezing and snow is scarce. Summer temperatures can rise to 30 °C and often the days are clear and hot, although recent summers have not been so dependable. Daily variations in temperature can be dramatic with hot sunny days being followed by night-time frosts. Above 500 metres, the climate is really sub-Arctic and it is dangerous for the inexperienced to venture into the mountains when the weather is doubtful. On the other hand, when one gets a beautiful day to explore the high tops it can be a truly unforgettable experience.

The flora and fauna of the district are very special because of the great diversity of wildlife habitats caused by the wide range of landforms and the high levels of semi-natural vegetation. It is an important area for natural heritage and contains many nature reserves and areas of special interest for nature. Red and roe deer are common while other animals include fox, badger, wild cat, otter, pine marten, red squirrel and blue hare, but most are often secretive and difficult to observe. Salmon, sea trout, brown trout, char and pike occur in the rivers and lochs. The bird life is outstanding and is described in the following chapters.

Bird Habitats of Badenoch & Strathspey

Rivers, Lochs and Marshes

The fast running rivers are crystal clear and subject to rapid changes in level after rains and snow melt. Dippers are well distributed on them and the shingle banks lower down provide nesting places for oystercatchers and common sandpipers with occasional ringed plovers and common terns. Crows and gulls scavenge for dead and stranded salmon after the spawning runs. Lower down where the rivers are slower moving, vegetation can be profuse with islands of wild lupins and riverside willows and alders. Red-breasted mergansers, goosanders, goldeneyes and mallard frequent these stretches along with common sandpiper, grey wagtail and dipper. Redpolls, sedge and willow warblers and a whole range of other passerines haunt the riverside trees and shrubs, while sand martins nest in the sandy river banks.

The hill lochs are often disappointing, with only a few common gulls and common sandpipers. The water of these lochs is cold, often acidic, and food is scarce. There are few birds at some of the larger, deeper lochs with rocky shores – the only additional species are oystercatchers and some waterfowl. A very few moorland lochans now have breeding red-throated divers. In contrast some of the forest and valley floor lochs are real gems, highly productive and reminiscent of boreal forest lakes in Sweden. So it's hardly surprising that birds like ospreys returned to live and nest beside these lochs. In summer, they support a variety of wildfowl, including tufted duck, as well as wading birds and other species associated with water like coots, little and slavonian grebes. The marshes which fringe the lochs and rivers can be very rewarding with breeding colonies of noisy black-headed gulls as well as mallard, wigeon, teal and tufted ducks, and waders such as redshank, snipe and curlew. Small birds include reed bunting, sedge and grasshopper warblers. In winter these places ring out to the calls of the wild swans down from Iceland.

Farm Land and Settlements
The high lying farm land is mainly for the rearing of high quality beef cattle and sheep with small scale cultivation associated with winter keep on crofts and small farms. Lower down the farms are larger and grow more cereals on the richer alluvial soils – oystercatchers, lapwings and golden plover, with snipe, redshanks and curlews in the wetter parts, occur on the farms. Wheatears, meadow pipits and skylarks can be common but usually nearer the moorland edge where a few twite can be occasionally found.

In autumn and winter the stubble fields are visited by greylag geese feeding on spilt grain along with rooks and jackdaws. Many of the smaller farms and crofts are surrounded by forests and by birch woodland, which is often used for sheltering cattle, so many woodland birds forage on the farm fields and nest in the woods.

Small birds flock together in and around settlements, especially chaffinches, with smaller numbers of yellowhammers, reed buntings and greenfinches. The farms are not now as valuable for small birds as in the past because corn stacks have been replaced by combine harvesters and there are not as many turnip fields.

Buzzards are a common sight nowadays on farm land and spend a lot of time, especially in winter, catching worms and beetles, while in summer they prefer young rabbits, of which there are plenty in this district. Small numbers of kestrels hunt over the rough pastures while sparrowhawks and hen harrier chase small birds. Around the houses and in the villages, there is now a plentiful supply of food at garden bird feeders. Greenfinches and siskins have increased in recent decades at the peanut holders and other birds include blue, great and coal tits as well as house sparrows, dunnocks and blackbirds. A few lucky people living near pine woods have crested tits coming to their bird tables. In summer, song thrushes frequent the gardens and swifts nest in the older houses. Occasionally in winter, waxwings come into the gardens to feed on cotoneaster berries.

Forest and Woodland

One of the greatest assets of the district is the remaining parts of the ancient Caledonian Forest of Scotland. The forests of huge spreading Scots pine, many over 200 years of age, have a rich hummocky forest floor of young pines, juniper bushes, blaeberry and heather, interspersed with birch, aspen, alder and rowan. Alas less than 1% of the original forests escaped the axe, fire and grazing, so the forests of Abernethy, Rothiemurchus, Kinveachy, Glen Feshie and others are very special indeed and have great historical significance as well. Birds are very well represented in these woods and three distinctive species are closely associated with Scots pine.

The largest is the capercaillie, with the male nearly as big as a turkey and just as magnificent as he struts in display on the spring leks. At the other extreme is the diminutive crested tit, grey-black with a black and white crest and a distinctive trilling call, so very Scottish that it is the emblem of the Scottish Ornithologists' Club. Scottish crossbills feed on the seeds in the tough Scots pine cones, the twisted bills are larger than the common crossbill, and they are specially adapted to the Scots pine. It is the only endemic bird species found in Britain. Other species which live in these forests include long-eared owl, sparrowhawk, redstart, tree pipit, treecreeper, goldcrest, siskin and chaffinch.

Plantations of larch, spruce and other pines grow in many places as commercial woods. Often these woods contain many of the species found in the old woods but the variety is not as high and sometimes the plantations are so dense that observation is difficult. Newly planted areas with trees the size of Christmas trees are temporarily interesting for a group of moorland edge species such as whinchat and occasionally short-eared owl. The birchwoods of Badenoch and Strathspey are very beautiful, fresh green in spring, richly golden in autumn and shimmering white with hoar frost in winter. Other deciduous woods include small areas of oak and beech, riverside stands of alder, bird cherry and willow, while rowan is widespread. Woodcocks, tawny owls and buzzards with a host of small birds, like willow warbler, redstarts, long-tailed tit and redpoll frequent these woods, with the occasional pied flycatcher and wood warbler. Some autumns, the rowan trees of the district are laden with red berries and these provide a plentiful harvest for redwings, fieldfares and many other species.

Moorland and Mountain
Heather moorland takes over at the woodland fringe, often with a

scatter of birches which is the best habitat for black grouse. Once heather is dominant and reasonably extensive then red grouse appear although not in former numbers. Many areas are still managed for grouse. Golden plovers, curlews and, especially in the west, greenshanks haunt the moors as do wheatears, meadow pipits and skylarks. These are good places to see peregrine falcons, merlins, golden eagles, hen harriers and short-eared owls as they hunt for birds and mammals. Mountain hares are common on some of the eastern moors but like many creatures in this habitat their numbers have declined rapidly in the last century. Hooded crows and a few ravens live in these areas while rocky outcrops support ring ouzels. In late summer and autumn, when the moorland plants among the heather are laden with berries, birds such as mistle thrushes and black grouse eat the fruit.

As the altitude increases red grouse thin out and when we reach a thousand metres ptarmigan take their place. Ptarmigan live on the high ground throughout their lives. Remarkably tame at times they can be hard to see and it's made more difficult by their annual moult to a white winter plumage. Often the hill tops are wide and rolling plateaux rather than jagged peaks, and these arctic-alpine areas are the home of dotterel, golden plover, skylark and meadow pipit. In rocky screes a few snow buntings build their nests and sometimes appear near the ski grounds in search of food, although they feed their young on insects often collected beside the remaining snow fields. Bird-watching on the high tops is very rewarding and well worth the climb. Take great care though, as these mountains look deceptively gentle but can be dangerous in quickly changing weather.

The Ornithological Year

The seasons in Badenoch and Strathspey can be extreme with severe frost and heavy snowfalls in winter. Six months later those short cold days are forgotten under hot summer skies. Some of the lowest temperatures in Britain have been recorded in this district. Wind speeds, too, can be excessive with gusts of well over 100 miles per hour being regularly recorded on Cairngorm, with the record so far being 172 mph on 20th March 1986. Most birds leave the Highlands in late summer and only the hardiest species are sedentary. In the severest winters some of these populations are drastically reduced by winter mortality. The following account gives a flavour of the ornithological highlights of the year in Badenoch and Strathspey.

January: It is often cold and snowy although some winters can be incredibly mild. Small bands of passerines, such as coal tit, crested tit, goldcrest and treecreeper roam the forests in search of hibernating insects. Farms and villages attract flocks of finches and buntings, and garden nut bags feed a host of tits as well as greenfinches, siskins and house sparrows. Occasionally a sparrowhawk will dash through attracted by the small birds. Wildfowl on the rivers and lochs include mallard, wigeon, goldeneye, tufted ducks and whooper swans, with greylag geese feeding on the larger farms beside the Spey. If lochs freeze over for more than a week most of the wildfowl leave for the coast. Red grouse, ptarmigan, golden eagle and raven live in the hills, with the grouse flocking up in very snowy weather.

February: The days are a little longer but still cold and snowy, and sometimes clear and beautifully crisp. The first mistle thrushes start to sing from high trees, rooks return to inspect their rookeries and some of the local birds, such as chaffinches, move back into the woods on warmer days. This can be a great month to combine

17

bird-watching and cross-country skiing, and there's also the chance of seeing an eagle sky-dancing in display.

March: Now the days are starting to warm up especially when the winds blow fresh from the milder south-west. Song thrushes and pied wagtails return while a real sign of approaching spring is the arrival of flocks of lapwings, oystercatchers and black-headed gulls. Many species, which have wintered on the coast return inland and the first true summer migrants, ring ousel and lesser black-backed gull, appear with wheatear, sand martin and osprey slipping in on the last days of the month.

April: Spring migration is in full swing with many waders and wildfowl reclaiming their nesting grounds. Ospreys start to rebuild their eyries, some of which have been damaged by winter storms, and to lay eggs. Chaffinches and many other woodland species are on territory and bird song increases daily. Black grouse and capercaillie are active at their leks while waders, wheatears and meadow pipits return to the moors. Late snow storms will send them scurrying back to the low ground for a day or two but the longer milder days soon melt any new snow. The northward passage of greylag geese and whoopers swans is under way, joined later in the month by pink-footed geese on their way back to Iceland. From mid month the birchwoods and scrubland resound to the lovely spring song of the willow warblers, accompanied later by many other summer visitors such as the swallow, redstart and cuckoo.

May: Nesting is now at a peak, with swifts and spotted flycatchers being the last of the migrants to arrive from Africa. The mountains tops are now clearing of snow, so ptarmigan are nesting, other summer visitors to the high tops, such as dotterel, are staking out their territories. Young birds of many species are starting to appear and the random late snows can be damaging to early nesters and fledglings. Occasional vagrants, such as red-footed falcon and black tern, can be recorded at this time of the year and small flocks of Canada geese fly over on their way north to moult on the Beauly Firth near Inverness.

June: This is a very beautiful month in Scotland, the days are incredibly long and the weather often perfect, warm, blue skies and little wind. Of course it can also be the opposite with even fresh snow on the mountains! The bird life of the district is enhanced by wild flowers, butterflies and young mammals such as roe deer fawns. Vegetation now in profusion makes it difficult to see some birds. Young birds are everywhere and it is a good month to hike into the mountains. The first flocks of waders, such as lapwings and oystercatchers start to congregate prior to moving back to the coast, and this reminds us that for some birds the nesting season is over for another year.

July: The remainder of the species fledge their young. Even those with long fledgling periods, such as ospreys and golden eagle, now have flying young. Many birds leave the area, in particular waders and gulls; others become difficult to observe as they skulk in long cover and undertake their annual moult. Small birds, such as warblers, tits, redstarts and tree pipits, gather together into noisy bands of squeaking young searching for food.

August: More birds depart but unlike spring they are not so easily observed. Suddenly one notices that all the swifts or spotted flycatchers have gone. Ospreys start their long journeys to Africa and by the end of the month most of the summer migrants have departed. Flocks of mistle thrushes often get mistaken for fieldfares as they forage on the moors for berries. Food is in fact plentiful and many birds take advantage of the annual harvest of fruit, such as cowberries and blaeberries.

September: The remainder of the summer visitors leave this month. Many local birds are much in evidence with young birds swelling their numbers. Capercaillies and black grouse are once more in view as the adults complete their moult and the young are flying. Wildfowl also emerge from their moult and congregate on the lochs, with goosanders families making Loch Garten their meeting place. By the end of the month the winter visitors are starting to arrive.

October: As the days get shorter and colder and the first snows start to fall in the mountains, there can be dramatic migrations of redwings and fieldfares from Scandinavia. Moving south, they can be seen voraciously devouring the rowan berries on their route. Greylag geese and whooper swans return from the Arctic. On still nights the evocative honking calls of the migrating geese can be heard mingling with the roaring of red stags at their annual rut.

November: The damp days of November reveal that most migrant birds have now departed although a few stragglers still pass through. The geese wintering in the valley are feeding on stubble fields during the day and flying to roost at night on the largest lochs, often joined by whooper swans. Reasonable sized flocks of ducks occur on some lochs; unlike the geese they fly out to feed on the fields at night. Some years waxwings occur around the villages.

December: All the species which are not going to spend the winter in the highlands have now gone and the local birds get down to the task of survival. Small flocks of redpolls and siskins forage in the birches. Bullfinches and crested tits can be found feeding in areas of long heather close to the woods, where they can find food even in deep snow. On the hills the stalkers are finishing the cull of red deer so ravens and eagles can sometimes get an easy meal from the remains. Ptarmigan and snow buntings are the only species to live on the high tops, often on the most exposed ridges where the wind has cleared away the snow. Even at the end of the year it's possible to get good bird-watching in the district. Capercaillie, black grouse, crested tit and Scottish crossbill are often easier to see now than in summer, while an interesting variety of wildfowl and small birds are present.

Late Dates for Migrants to Badenoch & Strathspey

It's always very special to see the first swallow of the spring or to hear one's first cuckoo of the year. This interest in early and late dates is common and for many people it deserves an entry in their diary, although first dates are more easy to record than the last for the year. The following list details the earliest and latest dates I have found recorded for Badenoch and Strathspey.

Summer Visitors	Earliest Date	Latest Date
Osprey	5th March 1988	16th December 1978
Ringed Plover	13th March 1974	5th October 1973
Dotterel	12th March 1961	7th September 1949
Redshank	2nd March 1976	28th August 1976
Greenshank	17th March	18th October
Wood Sandpiper	4th May	11th August
Common Sandpiper	3rd April 1972	2nd October 1976
Lesser Black-backed Gull	8th March 1977	24th September 1981
Common Tern	5th May 1980	4th August 1979
Cuckoo	11th April 1976	4th September 1979
Swift	2nd May 1980	12th November
Sand Martin	25th March 1977	29th September 1986
Swallow	11th April 1981	31st October 1987
House Martin	4th April	14th October 1980
Tree Pipit	12th April 1981	3rd October 1974
Redstart	10th April 1988	7th October 1969
Whinchat	21st April	27th October 1975
Wheatear	25th March 1972	31st October 1972
Ring Ouzel	25th March 1990	13th November 1983
Grasshopper Warbler	23rd April 1987	13th September
Sedge Warbler	24th April 1987	29th September 1972
Whitethroat	24th April 1987	17th August 1971
Garden Warbler	11th May 1990	7th September 1969
Wood Warbler	5th May 1985	mid August
Willow Warbler	11th April 1981	3rd October
Chiffchaff	6th April 1980	28th September 1972
Spotted Flycatcher	8th May 1962	19th September 1983
Pied Flycatcher	1st May 1984	17th August 1971

Places to Visit

Badenoch and Strathspey has many exciting and beautiful places for the visitor interested in birds, wildlife and the countryside, listed below are a selection of the main places to visit.

Abernethy Forest Nature Reserve (Royal Society for the Protection of Birds [RSPB]). Includes the famous Osprey Centre, at Loch Garten between Boat of Garten and Nethy Bridge. The Osprey Centre is open from late April to August from 10am to 8.30pm as long as the pair of ospreys are nesting; the visitor centre has high powered telescopes, live tv coverage of the nest, displays, shop and information. Other species can be seen from the hide, even the occasional capercaillie in spring. There are forest walks through the ancient Caledonian Forest with a chance to see crested tits, Scottish crossbill, goldeneyes, red squirrels and many other species. Full time wardens and information assistants. For further information and to arrange group visits contact the Warden, Grianan, Tulloch, Nethy Bridge, Inverness-shire PH25 3EF (Tel: 01479 831694, office hours only).

Insh Marshes Reserve (RSPB). Extensive flood plain mire between Kingussie and Loch Insh, with breeding and wintering waders and wildfowl, excellent place for whooper swans in winter; surrounded by woods, farmland and moors. Two hides over looking the marsh and a trail are accessible from the reception hide, near Ruthven Barracks on the B970 road. Open all days of the week, with the hides open 9am to 9pm or sunset. Full time Warden and assistants.

Cairngorms National Nature Reserve (Scottish Natural Heritage [SNH]). Superb reserve of 100 square miles of mountains and forests stretching from Strathspey to Deeside, including high mountain plateaux. Most of the land is in private ownership. Many tracks and paths. A wide variety of Strathspey's special birds, mammals and plants occur on the reserve. For reserve leaflets and information: Scottish Natural Heritage, Achantoul, Aviemore, Inverness-shire PH22 1QD (Tel: 01479 810477).

Craigellachie National Nature Reserve (SNH). A small reserve located directly behind Aviemore and accessed by an underpass under the A9 trunk road. A lovely walk through birch woods, with good views of the valley and an excellent place to watch peregrine falcons which regularly nest on the cliff above the path. Do not approach any closer to the cliff. For reserve leaflets and information: Scottish Natural Heritage, Aviemore, details as above.

Creag Meagaidh National Nature Reserve (SNH). This large reserve is situated on the north-west side of Loch Laggan, in the western edge of Badenoch, on the road from Kingussie to Fort William. A major programme of natural regeneration is leading to the rebirth of the native deciduous woodlands. Visitors can hike from the lochside to the mountain corrie using a well maintained trail. The reserve is open throughout the year and cars can be parked near the reserve headquarters at Aberarder Farm, where there is information or contact SNH staff at Aberarder Farmhouse, Kinlochlaggan, Inverness-shire (Tel: 01528 544265).

Dell Wood National Nature Reserve (SNH). This pine forest reserve is a part of Abernethy Forest and can be accessed by walks from Nethy Bridge. The typical wildlife of the old forest lives here, including red squirrel, crested tit and Scottish crossbill. Access is open and further information is available from SNH at Achantoul, Aviemore.

Glenmore Forest Park (Forestry Commission). Forest Enterprise operates a visitor centre at Glenmore, on the Aviemore to Cairngorm ski road, open 9am to 5pm daily. There are superb walks through the state-owned forests, including way-marked trails; most of the Caledonian forest wildlife occurs in these woods and a programme of native forest restoration is taking place. Forest Enterprise and the Scottish Wildlife Trust run a combined Ranger Service, with a programme of organised walks and events. Details from the visitor centre or get a copy of their *What's on Guide* available at the centre (Tel: 01479 861220).

Rothiemurchus Estate. Visitor centre and ranger service based at Rothiemurchus on the ski road from Aviemore. Regular guided walks, marked trails, superb scenery and natural habitats, including Loch an Eilein. Visit the fish farm for wildfowl and the best chance for seeing ospreys fish. Details of events and information at Rothiemurchus Visitor Centre, Aviemore (Tel: 01479 810858).

Landmark Visitor Centre, Carrbridge. Superb visitor centre set in the old Caledonian Forest on the edge of the village. Audio-visual shows, outdoor exhibitions, forest nature trail and viewing tower, shop and restaurant.

Highland Wildlife Park on the old main road between Kingussie and Aviemore; Scottish animals and birds past and present are on view in open surroundings, drive through access. Information centre and restaurant overlooking wildfowl loch.

Badenoch and Strathspey has a wide range of other facilities and visitor attractions, including professional guiding services for wildlife viewing and the outdoors. There is a full range of hotels, guest houses, self-catering cottages, bed and breakfast houses and campsites. Details of accommodation and events in the district from: Aviemore Tourist Office, Main Road, Aviemore, Inverness-shire (Tel: 01479 810363). Information on wildlife and reserves is sometimes available from the place where you are staying. Self-catering cottage and similar places on farms and country estates often have local information and private opportunities for walks.

Species Accounts

Accounts are given for all bird species which have been recorded in Badenoch & Strathspey, both recent and old records. I have made every attempt to include all published records but it is likely that important sightings have been missed, and of course visiting bird watchers may see interesting migrants in our area which are not subsequently reported. I would be very pleased to receive any records which materially update the following species list so that revisions can be made for any future edition of this book. Species are arranged in the standard format following the order in the *List of Recent Holarctic Bird Species* by K.H. Voous (1977). Bird names follow present usage and species which are clearly escapes from captivity are square-bracketed.

The account for each species starts with a brief summary of the recent status in Badenoch & Strathspey. It is important to remember that a species can be a rare visitor here but a common breeder on the shores of the Moray Firth, and sometimes vice versa. The terms I have used have the following meaning:

Breeding species

Common: over 500 pairs in most years
Numerous: 51–500 pairs in most years
Scarce: 11–50 pairs in most years
Rare: 1–10 pairs in most recent years
Occasional: has bred irregularly in last 30 years
Extinct: used to breed but no longer does so in this district
Introduced: released or escaped and breeding in the wild

Non-breeding visitors

Common: more than 500 in most years
Numerous: less than 500 in most years

Scarce: less than 50 in most years
Rare: 5–20 records
Vagrant: less than five records
Escape: captive birds seen in the wild

The species list includes information on birds up to the end of
1994.

Red-throated Diver *Gavia stellata*
(Rare breeder; scarce summer visitor, vagrant in winter)

A pair are supposed to have nested in Glen Einich about 1883.
From 1968, the species occurred as a rare but increasing visitor
between April and August. Visiting pairs at Loch Garten 27th
May 1972, 12 May 1978 and three Loch Laggan 26th June 1975,
suggested prospecting birds. A pair which nested successfully on
Dava Moor in 1978 was the forerunner of a very small breeding
population. A pair nested in the Laggan area in 1981 and in the
Cairngorms area in 1990. Three to four pairs now breed on small
moorland lochs. Food for the young is often carried from the
Moray Firth.

Red-throated Divers are present in the district from 8th
March to end of August. Summer visitors often frequent larger
lochs to fish and congregate; maximum count five Loch Morlich
5th June. First record Loch Insh 2nd April 1985, thereafter
annual with maximum of three on 25th June 1987. One late
record Loch Garten 13th November 1983.

Black-throated Diver *Gavia arctica*
(Irregular rare breeder; rare summer visitor and vagrant in winter)

A pair nested at Gaick 1909 and reported at Lochindorb in the last century. A pair nested unsuccessfully Loch Morlich 1934. A pair reared one young in 1968 at Gaick and were present but did not nest in 1969. A pair nested but failed near Kingussie in 1984. In 1988 a pair nested successfully on an RSPB artificial diver island on a loch in Badenoch, where unsuccessful nesting had been attempted, and has continued to nest there; in 1990 a second pair bred on an artificial island on another loch subject to flooding.

Black-throated Divers have occurred between 5th April and 16th September. Non-breeding pairs or single birds wander from loch to loch, e.g., four Loch Garten 19th May 1978 and four (same?) Loch Morlich 31st May 1978; four Loch Garten July 1992. One Loch Insh 6th December 1982.

Great Northern Diver *Gavia immer*
(Vagrant)

There have been four individuals (five records) since 1985: immature, Loch Insh 5–12 June 1985; adult, Loch Garten 12 July and Loch an Eilein 15–20 July 1985; one Loch Ericht 20 February 1987 and one Loch Insh 19 September 1987.

Little Grebe *Tachybaptus ruficollis*
(Scarce migrant breeder, rare in winter)

Breeds in small numbers on suitable low level lochs, including small forest lochans from Loch Insh to Grantown-on-Spey. No changes noted in distribution since last century. Arrives in March, earliest dates 7th, (1978, 1980) and 8th (1971, 1973); can be delayed to end of the month by cold weather. Starts nest building on arrival when already in summer plumage. Egg-laying from mid-April, early brood noted Rothiemurchus 8th May 1972.

27

Sometimes double-brooded with long breeding season; for example, small chicks at Loch Dallas 28th August 1973.

Maximum count 12 Loch Vaa 28th August 1973, most depart by mid-September but stragglers in October; three Insh Marshes 1st November 1977. One over-wintered Insh Marshes 1983–4. Out of season records on the river Spey near Kingussie 2nd January 1973 and two on 5th February 1993.

Great Crested Grebe *Podiceps cristatus*
(Rare visitor)

The nearest breeding site is at Loch Spynie in Moray. Single birds have been recorded on eight occasions at three lochs in Badenoch and Strathspey.

Loch Insh 20–23rd April 1970, 6th October 1988 and 16th September 1992. Loch Garten 4th June 1970, 15th May 1973, 11th April 1977 and 5th May 1980. Loch Vaa 29th June 1991.

Slavonian Grebe *Podiceps auritus*
(Rare migrant breeder)

A pair displaying near Newtonmore 23rd May 1963 did not stay to nest. Single birds Loch Insh and Loch Garten 1970. First bred in Strathspey in 1971 and then two to four pairs annually in the 1970s. Increasing in the 1980s to a peak of 10 pairs on six lochs in 1984 with an annual population of six to eight pairs. A further peak to 11 pairs on six lochs in 1991 and in recent years has averaged about eight pairs.

Arrives in late March, mainly early April (earliest 25th March 1989). Egg-laying early May to mid-July; a few cases of double-brooding, e.g. one pair with two young in each brood at one site 1983. Breeding success was often disappointing due to nest robberies in the earlier years but now has had some good years, for example 18 young reared in 1988. Departs August although some juveniles will linger until October.

Recorded as a migrant at Loch Insh in 10 years between 1973 and 1994; up to four in October, which included a late record on 20th October 1972.

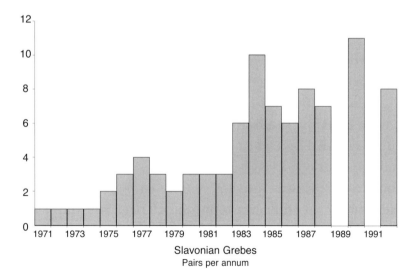

Slavonian Grebes
Pairs per annum

Black-necked Grebe *Podiceps nigricollis*
(Vagrant)

One Loch Garten 2nd October 1977.

Fulmar *Fulmarus glacialis*
(Vagrant)

Five records since 1972; three of them in June:
One flying from Ryvoan to Loch Morlich 13th June 1972.
One flying from Glenmore towards Cairngorm 6th February 1986.
One injured, recently fledged juvenile, Feshiebridge 15th September 1987.
One flying north of Braeriach 3rd June 1989.
One Loch an Eilein 15th June 1991.

Manx Shearwater *Puffinus puffinus*
(Rare visitor)

Eight records since 1973. Recently fledged juveniles, driven inland by bad weather, were found stranded at Kincraig, Loch Insh 30th September 1973, 17th September 1980 and 21st September 1991; Grantown-on-Spey 26th September 1979, Newtonmore 6th September 1983, Kingussie 16th September 1985 and Carrbridge 16th September 1985. Most were released unharmed at the coast.

Remains of an adult was found in a Peregrine eyrie near Cairngorm 12th June 1974.

Storm Petrel *Hydrobates pelagicus*
(Vagrant)

Single birds found freshly dead Boat of Garten 17th May 1962 and Nethy Bridge 3rd December 1981.

Leach's Petrel *Oceanodroma leucorhoa*
(Rare visitor)

There was an unprecedented arrival of about 20 storm-wrecked birds between 26th October and 2nd November 1952. One Loch Morlich 26th October, two on 2nd November; one Nethy Bridge 28th October. Six flew north over Newtonmore 29th October, one 30th, two 31st; one Kingussie 30th October, two on 1–2nd November. Single birds Loch Insh 30th October and 1st November; one Insh Marshes 1st November and one Boat of Garten 31st October. One found dead Abernethy 25th September 1990.

Gannet *Sula bassana*
(Vagrant)

Four records since 1976, three storm driven adults and one juvenile:
One flying north-east over Insh Marshes 17th May 1976.
One Loch Insh 1st July 1978.
One over Insh Marshes at Balavil 5th February 1989.
Juvenile stranded at Advie 4th October 1987, released Moray Firth next day.

Cormorant *Phalacrocorax carbo*
(Scarce annual visitor)

Mainly immature birds January to May and July to December; occasional adults, for example, two in breeding plumage flew west over Aviemore 6th April 1973 and two adults seen carrying sticks at Loch Insh 2–3rd May 1977. More frequently on Loch Laggan but no proof of breeding. Most often on larger lochs, such as Laggan, Insh and Lochindorb, usually one to two; maximum counts 10 Insh on 24th February 1977 and 30th September 1978. Nineteen Loch Insh in recent years. Regular roost in trees on Tom Dubh island, Loch Insh. One with plumage characteristics of continental race, *sinensis*, at Loch Insh April 1989. Immature ringed NW Sutherland, shot Loch Vaa April 1927.

Bittern *Botaurus stellaris*
(Vagrant)

One in reed beds at Invertromie marsh 1st January 1992 occurred in a winter when unusual numbers reached Scotland from the continent.

Little Bittern *Ixobrychus minutus*
(Vagrant)

Female beside river Spey between Boat of Garten and Kinchurdy 28th May 1973.

Grey Heron *Ardea cinerea*
(Scarce resident breeder and scarce migrant)

Well distributed and present throughout the year on rivers, marshes and lochs; visits highest glens and even on Cairngorms plateaux 24th July 1980. Old heronries recorded at Sluggan and Abernethy; Loch Mallachie heronry of 30 pairs in 1950s had been deserted by early 1960s. A heronry at Broomhill which had 30+ pairs in 1969 had decreased to 15 pairs in 1971. The Lynchat heronry increased from one to two nests in 1964–70 to 18 pairs in 1974, then decreased with final desertion 1980, when three pairs nested in low trees in Insh Marshes. The 1981–2 cold winter reduced numbers in the area and the 1985 survey revealed only three heronries holding 22–24 nests.

The population is now higher again with a recent heronry established near the Aviemore fish farm holding 28 nests in 1994. Most heronries are in Scots Pines although the Aviemore one is in larches. Maximum count away from nest site 45 Insh Marshes mid-April 1973. Numbers lower in winter, especially severe winters. Juvenile birds ringed in Cumberland and North Uist recovered at Kingussie July 1926 and October 1937 respectively.

White Stork *Ciconia ciconia*
(Vagrant)

One over Loch Insh 3rd May 1975.

Mute Swan *Cygnus olor*
(Rare resident breeder; rare summer visitor)

Not mentioned in the last century. One pair has nested Insh Marshes since at least 1961 with two pairs in some years, e.g., 1974, 1981, 1982; in 1972, seven young hatched on 3rd June and six survived to 28th September. Often unsuccessful and a total of only nine young reared between 1978 and 1981, although in the best year (1982), two pairs reared a total of nine young and there was also a non-breeding pair.

Single pairs nest at Loch Alvie and The Bogach. Mute Swans used to nest Boat of Garten in the 1950s and early 1960s, also in Tulloch in 1940s. One pair which nested Loch Mallachie 1974 was first for 20 years but they only lasted four years. Now rare at

Loch Garten with only two records between 1978 and 1994, including four in March 1992. In past non-breeders summered on various lochs, e.g. seven Loch Garten 10th July–8th August 1973. Birds occasionally visits remote lochs, one Loch Gharb-choire 12th April 1960, two Loch Broddain 13th July 1960. They remain in winter unless severe freezes, maximum 12 Loch Insh 16th December 1977, 10 Insh Marshes 5th December 1994; scarcer after severe winters of 1961–2 and 1962–3 but more after 1971. Numbers are lower in the recent decade. Usually feeds on freshwater but two juveniles were on Mains of Garten stubbles with Whooper Swans on 20th February 1967.

[Black Swan] *Cygnus atratus*
(Escaped vagrant)

Two adults and an immature Insh Marshes on 16th April 1994 and later two adults (same?) on 6th December 1994 had all escaped from a waterfowl collection.

Whooper Swan *Cygnus cygnus*
(Numerous winter visitor, October to April, mainly Insh marshes; rare in summer, possibly has bred)

Historically associated with Loch Insh; the kirk beside the loch is the 'the swan's chapel' and the Alvie kirk stands on 'the place of the swans'. Autumn arrivals from Iceland; three Loch Insh 19th September 1978, 68 Broomhill 22nd September 1978; usually from mid-October. Build up at Insh Marshes to autumn peaks of 106 on 24th November 1977, 150 on 13th December 1978 and 152 on 4th December 1981.

In most winters numbers decrease in January and then increase again to a higher spring peak. Maximum counts: 184 on

26th January 1976, 175 on 15th February 1974, 176 on 18th March 1981, 119 on 5th April 1977 and 208 in February 1993. Much display in March and April before departure; few in first week of May, largest count 23 on 2nd May 1979 and seven on 7th May. Last three Spey Dam 12th May 1985.

The other main but irregular wintering site, Boat of Garten-Nethy Bridge, where birds feed on stubbles and roost overnight on Loch Garten; maximum counts: 134 Loch Garten 1st March 1975, 26 in December 1977, 41 in November 1978, 121 on 6th December 1979; numbers now lower with a recent peak of 46 in November 1987. Some autumns a flock frequents the Laggan area, e.g. 80 in November 1983.

Single birds, usually injured, have summered in eight recent years with two in 1975. In 1967 a pair possibly bred on a hill loch while a pair were reported as nesting at Loch Insh in the 1920s. Darvic colour ringed birds from Iceland have been identified at Insh Marshes (three individuals) and one, which wintered Caerlaverock 1986–9, was at Insh February 1989.

Bean Goose *Anser fabalis*
(Vagrant)

One at Rothiemurchus 21st March 1970.

Pink-footed Goose *Anser brachyrhynchus*
(Common spring and autumn migrant, rarely stopping off on passage)

Spring migration mainly late April–early May (later than Greylags); maximum counts, 360+ flew NW Loch Garten 25th April 1961, 250 flew N Insh 2nd May 1978, 200 flew N Loch Garten 1st May 1971, 2,400+ flew N Insh Marshes 4th May

1983, 260 flew N Laggan 2nd May 1986. Early passage peaks: 102 flew NW Tulloch 28th March 1994 and 42 flew N Loch Garten 31st March 1978; some springs very scarce; latest record six Loch Garten 12th May 1968. Usual flyway of Drumochter–Corrieyarrick is to the west of the main Greylag route. Summer: single birds Loch Garten 2nd July 1985 and Boat of Garten 8th June 1994.

Autumn passage, earlier than Greylags; usually fast and high over the mountains, often at an altitude of several thousand feet; peak late September. Earliest, 10+ S over Loch Garten 6th September 1988; 45 Insh Marshes on 17th September 1978 and latest five Insh Marshes 12th December 1980. Peak counts: large skeins over Loch Garten 26th September 1963 into SW gale, more next morning; about 500 per hour south on five mile front Rothiemurchus 29th September 1969; 750+ flew south Aviemore 3rd October 1972; 100s at night Insh 26th September 1981; 600 S Tulloch 23rd September; 1,000 S Loch Garten 22nd September 1988; 830 S Tulloch 26th September 1989; 1,000+ S Insh 25th September 1993.

White-fronted Goose *Anser albifrons*
(Rare migrant; used to be scarce migrant)

Thirty flew west over Newtonmore 24th April 1919, 30 also flew NE on 30th April 1919; 32 south over Cairngorm 4th October 1964. Adult of Greenland race with Greylags on Loch Garten 6th March to 6th April 1974; one Greenland bird Loch Insh 1st November 1977, two Insh Marshes 5th November 1978, five on 20th February to 18th March 1982 and single birds on 12th April and 4th May 1983.

In recent years, 55 flew N Insh Marshes on 11th May 1984 and 11 on 14th November 1986. Single birds there on 18th

January and 15th November 1993 were first since 1986. One Loch Garten 15th November 1987 and one Laggan 5th April 1992. Twenty-two seen NE over Lurcher's Crag 24th November 1994.

Greylag Goose *Anser anser*
(Introduced scarce breeder; common spring and autumn migrant)

A feral flock released at Loch Laggan in 1969, peaked at 60 on 26th June 1975; these birds occasionally visited Insh Marshes and Loch Garten in summer. Birds from this source or from free flying birds at the Highland wildlife park first bred at Insh Marshes in 1983. Three pairs reared 17 young in 1984; increased to seven pairs by 1992. In 1990s spread further in the strath with up to three pairs at Boat of Garten pools; even a pair prospecting Tulloch 20th April 1994. Strong spring migration, usually flying N or NW, over the glens in April; earliest 18th March, latest 10th May. Peak counts over Loch Garten: 410 flew NW on 13th April 1972, 1,000 flew NW on 10th April 1973, 500 flew N on 16th April 1977 and 16th April 1979, and 600 flew N on 22nd April 1980. Numbers low some springs, especially in west; flocks sometimes rest in bad weather, for example 250 Insh Marshes 19th April 1973. Wintering birds now obscure migration flocks.

Autumn migration from late September, mainly October; earliest 17th September, last date uncertain because of wintering birds but well into December. Peak counts: 415 flew S Loch Garten 23rd September 1971, 1,000 flew S Insh 24th October 1972, 1,000 flew S Loch Garten 16th October 1979; total of 5355 passed south over Insh between 24th October and 27th November 1977. Sometimes scarce as in 1973.

Wintering numbers have increased since first regular flocks in 1970s, usually at Insh Marshes and Dulnain Bridge-Loch Garten, occasionally Laggan.

At Insh Marshes numbers have risen from 80 in November 1961 to wintering peaks of 1,000 on 23rd November 1978 and 782 in 1990–1 but large flocks tend to move on with around 100 remaining throughout the best winters.

The Loch Garten roost, which became regular in 1968, has increased from a peak of 120 in December 1968 to peaks of 1083 on 28th November 1978, 1,574 on 6th November 1986 and 1,724 on 15th November 1987. Numbers then dropped for several winters before peaking again to 1,300 in 1993. Numbers usually fall in December–January but in good years up to 400 may remain all winter. These geese feed on farm fields along the Spey and Dulnain between Aviemore and Grantown-on-Spey; occasionally they roost at night on Loch Pityoulish.

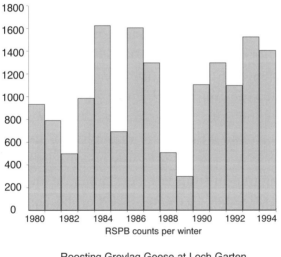

Roosting Greylag Geese at Loch Garten
Peak autumn counts

Snow Goose *Anser caerulescens*
(Vagrant)

Sixteen Lochindorb 27th August 1933 were undoubtedly escapes.

One flying north over Tulloch Moor 5th April 1959.

Canada Goose *Branta canadensis*
(Introduced: extinct breeder; scarce migrant)

A pair with six young at Gaick in early 1900's, one adult was shot. Birds on the annual moult-migration to the Beauly Firth from England, mainly Yorkshire, are recorded 2nd May–26th June and returning south 3rd August–24th September. Peak flocks recorded since first record at Loch Garten in 1969 are: 55 Glenmore 18th August 1973; 33 Loch Garten 22nd August 1977; 57 Loch Garten 18th August 1980; 80 Loch Insh 15th August 1981; 60 Loch Garten 27th August 1982; 64 Insh Marshes 13th August 1982; 41 Insh 7th June 1987 and 40 Dulnain river 27th May 1990. Outwith this pattern, seven Loch Laggan 17th July 1975; single Broomhill 24th February to 3rd March 1991 and at Insh Marshes 17th March 1991. A small Canada Goose at Insh Marshes 13th November 1994 may have been a genuine wild migrant from North America.

Barnacle Goose *Branta leucopsis*
(Rare migrant)

First record Insh Marshes 21st October 1961, two Loch Insh 23rd October 1982 and three Loch Garten 24th October 1982., 11 records Insh Marshes since 1982, usually one or two, in September (two), October (four), December, January, February and April. One feral bird June 1993–March 1994. Single birds at Loch Garten 2nd April 1984, May and June 1992; Dulnain Bridge 21st February–31st March 1984; over Cairngorm 10th October 1988; Nethy Bridge 27th October 1989 and Broomhill 14th February 1992. Three Loch Laggan 15th October 1990.

Brent Goose *Branta bernicla*
(Rare migrant)

One dark-bellied bird Loch Insh 30th November 1976; flock of
35 attacked by Peregrine Falcon over Loch Mallachie 25th
September 1977 and five Loch Mallachie in September 1986.

Red-breasted Goose *Branta ruficollis*
(Vagrant)

Adult at Invertromie flood meadows 9th–19th March 1994, often
feeding with oystercatchers, moved to the fields beside the river
Spey near Broomhill – Dulnain Bridge 22nd March and stayed
with the greylag flock into April. The winter of 1993–4 saw a
strong influx of this eastern species into western Europe.

Shelduck *Tadorna tadorna*
(Scarce migrant)

First record was at Kincraig on 26th March 1969, then five Loch
Garten 25th April and two on 17th May 1973. Sixteen records at
Insh Marshes and Loch Insh between 1969 and 1994, recorded in
February, March (four), April (four), June (three), July, August,
September and December; mainly one or two, but six on 31st
March 1990 and three Loch Insh 7th December 1978.

Recent single birds at Loch Garten on 17–21st November
1984, 24th November 1987 and two in July 1991. Five Loch
Morlich 9th February 1989. Two Avielochan 8th December
1992.

[Mandarin] *Aix galericulata*
(Escape vagrant)

Three records of four birds since 1985:
Male Loch Garten 23–25th October 1985.
Pair at Loch Vaa 6th May 1990, male on 7th–13th May 1990.
One Newtonmore April 1992.

American Wigeon *Anas americana*
(Vagrant)

A drake on the river Spey at Broomhill in February and March 1990 was seen at Loch Garten on 1st March 1990.

Wigeon *Anas penelope*
(Scarce breeder; common winter visitor)

Well distributed as a breeder on marshes, lochs and forest lochans. Good numbers were breeding in 1895 and in the best of recent years about 50 pairs nested in area. Population fluctuates, for example, at Insh Marshes numbers were down to three to four pairs in 1980, from a peak of 15–20 pairs in 1975 but 37 pairs in whole area of the marshes in 1992. Ducklings on water from 22nd May, mainly early June. Duckling ringed at Insh Marshes 1934, was shot in Co. Mayo, Eire, February 1935 and another ringed at Boat of Garten 1960, shot in Gironde, France, 7th September 1960.

Usually winters at Insh Marshes and sometimes on other lochs depending on weather. Peak counts include: 300 Loch Garten 29th October 1961, 45 Laggan and 120 Loch Mor, Dulnain Bridge 1st November 1961. Duck numbers were very high in the early 1960s. 200 Insh Marshes 28th March 1975, 177 Loch Garten 25th November 1978. Less than 100 in poor years of 1977, 1979 and 1980. Recent peaks at Loch Garten of 327 on 26th January 1989, 500 in February 1992 and 540 in February 1993.

Gadwall *Anas strepera*
(Extinct breeder; rare visitor, none since 1983)

Nest found at Inshriach and a pair probably bred Abernethy 1942; pair nested successfully Loch Morlich 1953. Female Loch Garten 15th April 1971; female Glenfeshie 22nd May 1974; two Insh Marshes 31st October 1977; male Glentruim 26th May 1981 and female Insh Marshes 3rd April 1983.

Teal *Anas crecca*
(Numerous breeder; and numerous winter visitor)

Well distributed but thinly spread breeder from Lochindorb to Loch Laggan. Mainly in marshes and on larger lochs. Best site is Insh Marshes where census gave 38–45 pairs Insh Marshes in 1976 and 86 pairs on the whole of the marshes in 1992. Also nests in forest lochans and bogs, even in highest glens to 500 metres a.s.l.. First broods on water from 18–19th May.

Many depart in severe weather but good numbers, including migrants, winter. Peak counts at Insh Marshes: 150 on 26th March 1975, 200 on 28th September and 350 in November 1976, 230 on 8th November 1979, 500 (best ever) on 19th October and 250 in November 1981; usually 100–300 in 1990s. Elsewhere: 100 Loch Garten 30th October 1961, 146 on 25th November 1978 and 150 in September 1983; declined since with peaks below 50. Duckling ringed North Iceland 1950 was shot Kingussie 28th December 1950.

A drake of North American race *A.c.carolinensis*, the Green-winged Teal, seen west of Newtonmore on 19–27th May 1979.

Mallard *Anas platyrhynchos*
(Common resident breeder and winter visitor)

Breeds throughout the district, even into higher glens to 500 metres a.s.l.; 60–70 pairs nested Insh Marshes reserve in 1976 but usually 150–200 pairs on extended reserve in 1980s with peak count of 275 pairs on whole of the marshes in 1992. Ducks start to lay in March and early April (earliest eggs recorded 3rd March) and earliest ducklings recorded 4th April. In recent decades artificially reared birds have been released in several areas for shooting.

At least 400 winter Insh Marshes, peak counts include: 400+ on 24th November 1962, 500 in October 1973, 650 on 3rd December 1976, 475 on 16th February 1980 and 682 in December 1992. Flocks occur elsewhere; peak counts include: 475 Loch Garten 12th November 1978, 351 on 11th October 1980 but most years below 200, although 320 in 1989. Other counts include 200 Loch Mor, Dulnain Bridge 1962; 200 Lochan Mor, Rothiemurchus 13th November 1962; 112 Loch Alvie 5th November 1972 and 300 Rothiemurchus fish farm 16th August 1994. One ringed Wigtownshire 10th February 1928 was shot at Boat of Garten 31st August 1930, while a duckling ringed Rothiemurchus 17th July 1963 was shot at Boat of Garten in September 1963.

Pintail *Anas acuta*
(Rare sporadic breeder; scarce summer visitor)

In 1971 a pair nested Insh Marshes and possibly again in 1976 and 1983. One to two recorded annually 1968–94 mainly January to May, but also June to December. Max five on 11th October 1991.

Elsewhere: four Loch Garten 26th March 1984 and two on 25th April 1984; single birds Loch Morlich 19th February 1989 and Broomhill 6th January 1991.

Garganey *Anas querquedula*
(Extinct breeder; rare visitor)

A nest containing six eggs was found in an unnamed marsh by the Spey in 1947, nearby were two drakes and a duck. More recently, a pair Insh Marshes 18–20th May 1977 with male to 27th May; male Insh Marshes 27th June 1978 and female on 1st July 1978. Female Boat of Garten 7th June 1981 and another female Boat of Garten 28th July 1988.

Shoveler *Anas clypeata*
(Rare breeder; scarce visitor)

Pair at Insh Marshes 18th April 1877 and this is still the only regular breeding haunt. Arrives late March, early dates 24th February 1980, 7th and 19th March. Usually one to four pairs to 1984, nowadays up to five pairs annually. Young can be late, brood of eight young seen 19th July 1979, also brood of eight young on 14th June 1992. Maximum counts 18 Loch Insh October 1972 and 12 on 7th November 1978. Usually departs late September to early November. Occasionally seen Loch Garten: pair 11th May 1970, pair 8th May 1971; male on 11th May 1974, two late May 1978 and four November 1983. Male Boat of Garten 21st May 1990.

Pochard *Aythya ferina*
(Rare occasional breeder; scarce visitor)

A pair nested Loch Insh 1914, when young seen on 1st July; and 1978, when female and four young seen 26th June. Normally arrives in July and August, early ones are usually drakes, earliest date four males Loch Garten 8th July. Winter flocks build up in autumn, moving from loch to loch; many leave in severe weather with spring dispersal in March, latest 16th April.

Maximum counts: 36 (seven females) Loch Morlich 13th October 1971 and 43 (12 females) on 16th October 1972; 40 Loch Alvie 12th November 1969 and 22 on 24th November 1962; numbers lower since 1973 maximum 24 Loch Insh 9th November 1975 and 14 on 7th December 1979 but 43 on 15th December 1982. Further decline since 1984; maximum 21 Loch Insh 14th February 1987 and 23 on 13th December 1990, usually less than 10. Other peak counts: 12 Loch Garten 10th February 1987; 17 Loch Morlich 18th November 1988, 33 there on 9th February 1989 and 20 Loch Alvie 15th November 1989. Males outnumber females by about three to one.

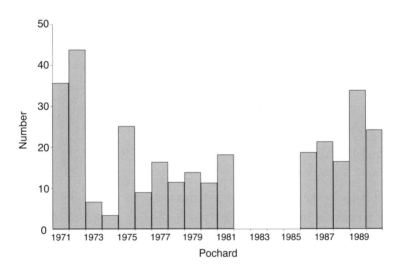

Pochard

Ring-necked Duck *Aythya collaris*
(Vagrant)

Records of this North American vagrant almost certainly relate to three individuals:
Adult drake first seen Loch Insh and marshes 15th February 1980

to 30th March and 12th November to 31st December 1980, moved to Loch Mallachie 13th April 1980 and at Grantown-on-Spey 28–29th December; returned to Insh Marshes 1st January to 31st March and on 10th November 1981, 25th February 1982 and 22nd March–7th April, 1–3rd June and 3–20th November 1983 and was present, usually most often seen Loch Insh October to April, until 7th February 1985.

Drake first seen Loch Insh 2nd October 1988, probably a new bird. Wintered at Insh and Loch Morlich and seen Loch Garten 8–10th April 1989. At Loch Insh 2nd February 1990 and then Pityoulish and Loch Vaa February and March, summered at Rothiemurchus fish farm in 1990, November and December at Loch Morlich. Seen throughout 1991 at four lochs; in 1992 at loch Insh in January and at Loch Morlich and Loch Vaa to end of the year; in 1993 at the fish farm in April and at Loch Morlich in October; and in 1993 at Loch Insh on 4th December.

A female seen with the second drake at Loch Morlich 29th October to 6th December 1992.

Tufted Duck *Aythya fuligula*
(Numerous breeder)

In the 1970s about 75 pairs on low-level lochs and marshes, probably some decrease in recent years. Thirty-seven pairs Insh Marshes in 1992. Present throughout year on larger lochs and rivers, except in severe weather. Breeders return to smaller nesting lochs in March; first young seen 30th May to 12th June; breeding success at Insh Marshes ranging from 38 broods containing 200 young on 5th July 1977 to only 47 young in 1981. Peak counts include 100 Insh April 1974 and 66 on 6th May 1975; 30 Loch Garten 14th August 1977 (decline there since) and 22 Loch Morlich 13th October 1971.

Scaup *Aythya marila*
(Scarce migrant, usually in spring)

A pair Rothiemurchus June 1952 and four (three females) Loch
Garten 2–4th May 1966. Between 1973 and 1994, 20 records in
13 years at Loch Insh; usually one or two in all months except
April, June and December, mostly September and October; but
seven Loch Insh 30th September 1981, eight on 26th September
1987 and 10 on 9th August 1992.

    Pair Loch Morlich 23–31st May 1978 and one there
September–December 1992; six Loch Garten November 1990 and
maximum four Loch Garten in June–October 1992.

Long-tailed Duck *Clangula hyemalis*
(Scarce autumn migrant; rare in spring)

One shot Loch Insh 13th November 1908. Single birds at Loch
Insh 11th October 1973, 25th October 1978, 9th November
1981 and 6th December 1982. Further 11 records in period
October to December between 1984 and 1994, all single birds
except three on 23rd October to 22nd November 1988. Male
Spey Dam 9–10th November 1975. One Loch Garten 4th
November 1984, three there on 20th October 1988, six on 21st,
one to two to 20th November; one on 11th October 1992. One
Loch Morlich 5–6th November 1988. Spring: single drakes at
Loch Garten 14th April 1986 and Loch Insh 22nd May 1987.

Scoter *Melanitta nigra*
(Rare visitor)

A pair at Spey Dam 12th May–2nd July 1981. Seven (four males)
Loch Insh 4th May 1983; female there 17th September 1984;

seven females on 4th November 1984, two on 25th October 1986 and a drake 3rd May 1987. Female Loch Alvie 14th June 1986 and a pair on 22nd July 1987. One Loch Morlich 23rd November 1990.

Surf Scoter *Melanitta perspicillata*
(Vagrant)

Adult male at Loch Insh 14th October 1979.

Velvet Scoter *Melanitta fusca*
(Vagrant)

Female on Loch Insh 8th October 1971.

Goldeneye *Bucephala clangula*
(Numerous recent breeder, and a numerous winter visitor)

Used to arrive in early October from Scandinavia and winter on lochs and river Spey in good numbers; much display in spring and pre-migratory flocking, maximum count 46 Loch Morlich 27th April 1960. Birds often lingered into May, even in the last century, one Loch Insh 20th May 1895, but an increase in records from the early 1960s.

Some nesting boxes were erected in the 1950s for this species and Goosander. The RSPB started a major nest box scheme throughout the Highlands in 1961 and a pair of Goldeneye first nested in one of these boxes at Loch an Eilein in 1970 and reared four young.

This pair nested again in 1971 and 1972; increased to three pairs in 1973 and then annual increases to 41 in 1981, 54 in 1984, 85 in 1989, 95 in 1990 and is now well over 130 pairs.

Most of the ducklings are taken to the river Spey and survival has been good. Goldeneyes are now one of the commonest ducks on many lochs. Please do not disturb or remain near the nest boxes in April and May or else the feeding females cannot get back to their nests.

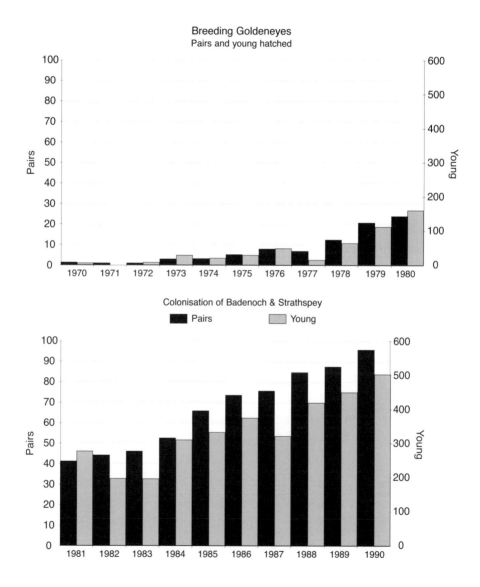

Breeding Goldeneyes
Pairs and young hatched

Colonisation of Badenoch & Strathspey

Maximum flock counts include 100 Loch Insh January 1973, 60+ Loch Insh 26th March 1975, 124 there in March 1993 and 165 in November 1994. Fifty-two Loch Garten 10th March 1977 and 62 there in March 1987. Fifty Loch Morlich 1980.

Smew *Mergus albellus*
(Vagrant)

Drake Lochindorb 7th February 1912.
One female or immature Loch Insh 3rd April 1979.
One female or immature Insh Marshes 2nd February to 14th March 1983.
Adult drake Kingussie and Insh Marshes 7 December 1983 to 27th April 1984.
Adult drake Loch Insh and Marshes 11th January to 29th May 1985.
One female-immature Loch Insh 13th November 1994.

It is believed that the 1983, 1984 and 1985 records may refer to the same bird returning to the Insh Marshes. In spring 1985 it was observed displaying to female Goldeneyes and on 12th May it was at Uath Lochans with two females near their nesting sites. Hybrids of these two species are known and singles have occurred at Inverness in the winters of 1984 and 1987–8.

Red-breasted Merganser *Mergus serrator*
(Scarce migrant breeder; rare in winter)

Breeds in small numbers, mainly by the Spey and on the larger lochs. Arrives in spring from late March or early May (earliest 13th March); pairs gather at dusk to display on lochs, such as, Loch Garten where peaks of four pairs 16th April 1963, nine on 15th May 1980 and 23 in April 1983. Maximum at Loch Insh 15 in May 1983. First chicks usually early July, broods can congregate on rivers. Males go to the coast to moult in July, females follow when young can fly. Occasionally visits lochs in October and November, maximum 12 Loch Garten 11th November 1979. One January record.

Goosander *Mergus merganser*
(Scarce breeder, regular in winter)

When the species started to colonise the British Isles at the end of the last century, probable breeding was recorded in this district in 1878 and definitely in 1892. Increased this century. Breeds in small numbers throughout the area near rivers and lochs, but more pairs and more widely distributed than Red-breasted Merganser. Nests in holes in trees even on smallest rivers and lochans, recorded to 500 metres a.s.l.. Sometimes in nest boxes. Numbers not well known; usually one to two pairs Insh marshes reserve but five pairs in 1992.

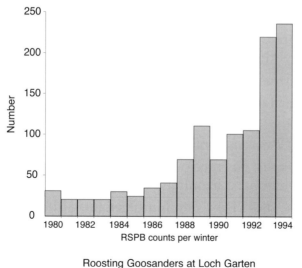

Roosting Goosanders at Loch Garten
Peak autumn counts

Tends to arrive in late February and congregates on larger lochs and rivers in March and April to display and roost; 24 Loch Insh 21st February 1980; females lay eggs from mid-April. Drakes congregate, for example 15 males, Loch Garten late April 1962, before emigrating in June to moult in northern Norway. Females and young go to Moray Firth.

Often present in October to December, occasionally present all winter; previous peak counts 25 Loch Garten 15th October 1980 and 24 on 21st February 1980; 20 Insh 22nd December 1977; 25 Loch Insh December 1983. Big increase in September roost flocks, since mid 1980s, at Loch Garten where annual peak counts of 70 on 12th September 1988, 87 on 3rd September 1987, 226 in September 1993 and 233 in September 1994. Then numbers much lower in October–December.

Ruddy Duck *Oxyura jamaicensis*
(Vagrant)

Birds from the English feral population of this North American duck started to breed in Scotland in 1979 and are colonising the country. There are three records since 1987:
Drake Kinchurdy 30th May to 6th June 1989.
Female Loch Garten 7–8th June 1989.
One Loch Garten 1st July 1992.

Honey Buzzard *Pernis apivorus*
(Rare summer visitor; has bred)

One killed Carrbridge May 1855 and several other records in latter part of nineteenth century suggest that they bred. Single sightings over the years include Aviemore 1st August 1970, Loch Insh 29th May 1971, Boat of Garten 17th July 1974 and 15th

June 1975, Cairngorm 3rd July 1988, Nethy Bridge 1st
September 1989 and Insh 16th August 1992.

Red Kite *Milvus milvus*
(Extinct breeder; vagrant and now rare visitor)

Used to breed, probably in reasonable numbers. Birds and eggs
were collected for museums in the latter part of the nineteenth
century. These included a male shot in Abernethy in 1876, two
females shot off the nest in 1876, four chicks taken from one nest
and three eggs from the other. A woodcutter felled the tree
containing a fourth nest in 1876. In 1878 a pair nested in
Rothiemurchus but the species was probably extinct in this area
by 1892.

Single birds reported 1933 and 1952. One wintered near
Laggan 9th January to 5th February 1972 and one Loch Garten
15th August 1978.

Following the re-introduction of young Swedish Red Kites to
the Black Isle near Inverness by the RSPB, wandering birds have
visited the valley. Records include three which spent the 1990–1
winter around the Insh Marshes, one of these was present from
29th August 1990 to 23rd March 1991. There have been other
records at Kingussie, Newtonmore, Abernethy, Nethy Bridge,
Grantown-on-Spey, Dulnain Bridge and Carrbridge between 1991
and 1994.

White-tailed Eagle *Haliaetus albicilla*
(Extinct breeder; rare visitor)

A pair used to breed in previous centuries at Loch Laggan. One
killed Carrbridge June 1854 and an adult flying up river at
Aviemore 23rd May 1927.

More recently wandering birds have been seen following the re-introduction of young Sea Eagles to Rum 1975–84 by the Nature Conservancy Council and in 1993 and 1994 by Scottish Natural Heritage, and their successful breeding in the Western Highlands and Islands. A two year old at Insh Marshes on 12th October to 12th November 1985 had been released on Rum in 1984, while a three year old at Tulloch on 27th October 1993 was wild bred from the west coast. Juveniles seen in recent years have been from the 1993 release while birds in adult plumage have been seen near Boat of Garten in March 1993 and at Kingussie on 26th June 1993.

Marsh Harrier *Circus aeruginous*
(Scarce summer visitor)

Birds, principally immatures or females, have been recorded almost annually Insh Marshes since first on 21st May 1966. Mostly present for short periods but some have been long staying. For example: pair, (male, a first year), from 22nd May to 20 September 1966; pair 25–26th June and adult female 8th July –22nd August 1977; male 27th April–13th May then female 13th May–14th September, another male 19th June–24th August 1988. Earliest date 27th April 1988, latest 20th September 1966. Other single birds: Loch Garten 24–25th July 1979; Tulloch Moor 16th May 1982; Laggan 7th May 1988; Pityoulish 21st May 1988; Loch Mallachie 6th June 1990 and Dalnavert 4th July 1994.

Hen Harrier *Circus cyaneus*
(Rare breeder; scarce winter visitor)

Used to breed but persecution extreme in the last century and no records of breeding from 1857, when nest of five young taken at

Carrbridge, to 1936 when a pair nested at Abernethy. Since then has increased, especially near new forestry plantations, but even so scarce and thinly distributed. Still illegally persecuted on grouse moors in some areas.

Seen over farms on low ground outwith breeding season. Roosts communally in winter and at best known site at Insh Marshes, has peaked at 13 birds in 1988 and 1991 and 16 in November 1990 with average numbers of five in 1970s and 10 in recent years. Occasionally seen at high levels; one at the Yellow Moss in September at 700 metres a.s.l.; Carn Ban Mor 19th May 1990 and Larig Ghru 13th October 1990.

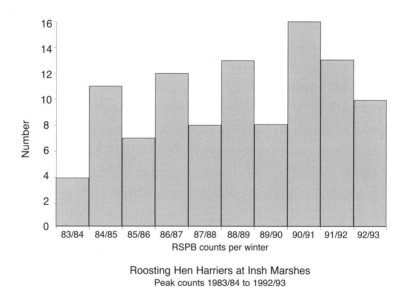

Roosting Hen Harriers at Insh Marshes
Peak counts 1983/84 to 1992/93

Goshawk *Accipiter gentilis*
(Extinct and sporadic breeder; scarce visitor)

Used to breed but exterminated in latter half of nineteenth century. Has been recorded from early 1950s in very small numbers but believed to have been escaped falconer's birds. More from early 1960s, including released birds. Nesting has been attempted but successful records are very rare. Nowadays seen annually in very small numbers; for example, at Insh Marshes has been identified in six years between 1977 and 1994, most in August.

Sparrowhawk *Accipiter nisus*
(Resident scarce breeder)

Well distributed but thinly throughout all woodlands; often visits gardens, especially outwith nesting season. Six to eight pairs recorded in Rothiemurchus and Inshriach in 1952 and one pair estimated per 1,000 acres of woodland in 1968. Decreased in main pesticide era 1960s and 1970s but population now back to normal although very variable. For example at Insh reserve it was recorded on 89 bird/days in 1977, 39 bird/days in 1978 and 56 bird/days in 1979, with maximum day count since then of six in February 1991. One on Cairn Lochan 20th July 1990.

Buzzard *Buteo buteo*
(Numerous resident breeder; numerous migrant)

Excessive persecution in the last century. Thought to be extinct in Abernethy from 1850. There was only one pair in the area in the 1920s at Inshriach, otherwise none until an increase from 1945. A pair at Pityoulish in 1952 since when the species has increased, although in some areas persecution lasted into the 1980s. Decreased in Abernethy forest from six pairs in early 1960s to one to two pairs in 1970s but now increased again to previous numbers. Thirty–three pairs were recorded in a study area between Boat of Garten and Kingussie in 1969 and there are probably more now given that 12 pairs nest in the Insh Marshes area alone. Movements of ringed juveniles from Spey study area to central Scotland in winter and one from Drumnadrochit killed near Grantown-on-Spey. Counts: 17 soaring over Kingussie area 16th September 1981 and 24 in September 1987.

Rough-legged Buzzard *Buteo lagopus*
(Rare migrant)

Only eight records (seven birds) of this winter visitor from Scandinavia shows that this area is away from the more easterly migration route of this species in Scotland:
One killed Belleville, Kingussie 18th December 1891.
One Ord Ban, Rothiemurchus 7–9th March 1961.
One Dalwhinnie 22nd February 1969.
One Kingussie 20th December 1969.
Two over the Slochd 29th October 1979.
One Tulloch Moor 16th June 1985.
One Tore Hill, Tulloch 10th March 1986.
One over Ryvoan, Glenmore 13th March 1989 and over Cairngorm on 14th.

Golden Eagle *Aquila chrysaetos*
(Scarce resident breeder, some passage of immature birds)

Traditionally about 20 home-ranges in district, although hunting ranges extend over watersheds. Some eyries no longer regularly used due to persecution and more recently by human disturbance. Some home-ranges have become amalgamated through effects of long term degradation due to over-burning and over-grazing by sheep and red deer. Mainly in the mountain areas, but a few eyries in trees and birds may occur from valley floor to highest peaks. One lower ground site recolonised in recent decade.

Away from nest sites, birds seen Insh Marshes in 14 out of 21 years to 1994; best year was five records in 1988; more often young birds seen, although two adults on 21st May 1989. A colour-tagged immature seen near Dalwhinnie on 2nd June 1986 had been ringed as an eaglet in Morvern. The best chance to see eagles is to drive to higher remote public roads; sit down in a place with a broad vista and scan the hill tops with binoculars; do not visit nests.

Osprey *Pandion haliaetus*
(Rare summer visitor and breeder)

The famous Osprey observation post at Loch Garten is open April to August. The recorded history of the Osprey in Strathspey dates back to at least 1804, and in the nineteenth century about three sites were regularly occupied by breeding Ospreys with possibly another two sites used less frequently. The most famous site was on Loch an Eilein Castle where there were breeding records between 1808 and 1899 and visiting birds until April 1902.

Other nesting sites mentioned in the last century are Loch Morlich, Loch Gamhna, Strathnethy, Abernethy and Loch Insh. Sadly, the history was one of ruthless persecution. The fate of 24 nests at Loch an Eilein between 1846 and 1899 is known. The eggs were robbed 13 times, the birds were twice disturbed and gave up, and once one was shot. Young were hatched in eight years but only twice were known to fly. It is surprising that they managed to continue to nest until 1899 and part of this perseverance was due to the efforts of the Grants of Rothiemurchus in trying to protect them.

In 1930 an Osprey was killed by flying into an overhead wire at the Spey bridge, Grantown-on-Spey on 17th September. Single birds were seen in 1936, 1937 and a pair at Loch Garten in 1939. There was an increase with single birds in May 1947, 1950, 1951, 1952 and one was shot at Kingussie 1948. Records became more frequent in the early 1950s, with rumours of breeding in 1952, three were seen on 29th August 1953 and finally a pair nested near Loch Garten in 1954, rearing two young.

A pair nested again in 1955 at Loch Garten but deserted and moved to a new nest. The next year the eggs disappeared while only one bird was seen in 1957. A pair nested again at Loch Garten in 1958. Despite the RSPB setting up a wardening scheme the eggs were stolen at night. In 1959 Ospreys nested successfully at the new site at Loch Garten and this site has been in use ever since. Successful nesting has occurred in 29 years with a total of 63 young fledgling. A second pair nested in the area in 1963 and since then the population in Badenoch and Strathspey has increased in line with the Scottish population which now stands at 95 pairs.

Ospreys can be seen fishing on many lochs and rivers in the district, with one of the best places in recent years being the ponds at the Rothiemurchus fish farm. Most occur between 1st April and mid September, the earliest date being 5th March, most have gone by late August with stragglers into September to 29th; late migrants Rothiemurchus 13th November 1980 and Nethy Bridge to Grantown-on-Spey 30th November to 16th December 1978.

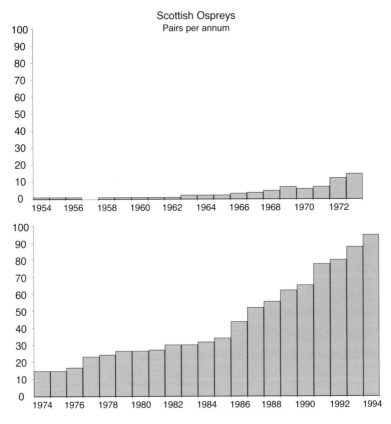

Scottish Ospreys
Pairs per annum

Kestrel *Falco tinnunculus*
(Scarce resident breeder and migrant)

Breeds thinly throughout area, in cliffs and in tree nests of other birds, mainly in the valley floor but occasionally on higher ground to 700 metres a.s.l.. Sgoran Dubh 1962 and Gaick 1968. The species was scarce in 1952 due to persecution but increased in the 1960s when 35 pairs found in 200 square miles. Numbers vary

60

from year to year, for example one to two pairs Garten reserve 1977–80 but five pairs in 1981 (three in nest boxes). Display at nest cliffs from mid-March; eggs laid from late April.

Young birds move out in August and September, when they also occur in high mountains, two immatures Cairngorm plateaux August 1972. Juveniles ringed Boat of Garten to Kingussie have been recovered in autumn–winter in France (two), Spain and southern England. Adult females also tend to move returning in March, while wintering birds tend to be adult males although some of these may be immigrants from Scandinavia.

Red-footed Falcon *Falco vespertinus*
(Vagrant)

Three records of this eastern European insect eating falcon have occurred since 1961; the second on Tulloch Moor was seen only 200 yards from where I found the previous bird 31 years earlier.
A female Tulloch Moor 15–16th May 1961; seen catching caterpillars in the heather.
Adult male Duthil 29th May 1992.
Immature female Tulloch Moor 1–3rd June 1992.

Merlin *Falco columbarius*
(Scarce breeder and migrant)

Twenty to 30 breeding areas; mainly on heather slopes or lower mountains, rarely on high ground; usually nests on ground but some records of tree nesting in old crow nests. Numbers are lower now than in the 1960s. Breeding pairs return to traditional areas in March and leave in August; passage birds seen throughout district, rarely in winter. Most often seen in late summer when young birds hunt moorland passerines, often in unsuccessful aerial pursuits. At Insh Marshes, a scarce migrant with single records in all months, although two in September 1983 and three on 7th April 1987. Single birds at summit of Cairngorm 13th March and 12th April 1990.

Hobby *Falco subbuteo*
(Scarce summer migrant)

One Loch Garten 15th May 1960. Eight single birds in June–August in seven years between 1963 and 1973, and five single birds 1977–83 between 23rd June and 22nd August. Since 1984, about ten records at Insh Marshes, all in September except for single birds in May 1989 and October 1994, with two birds in 1987. Single birds at Loch Garten 7th September 1988 and 26–31st May 1989; Grantown-on-Spey 25th June 1987 and Carrbridge 10th June 1988

[Lanner Falcon] *Falco biarmicus*
(Escape vagrant)

One over Insh Marshes in May 1982 was considered to be a falconer's bird.

[Saker Falcon] *Falco cherrug*
(Escape vagrant)

One at Corriechullie, Dorback 26th August 1973 was considered to be a falconer's bird.

Gyr Falcon *Falco rusticolus*
(Vagrant)
Four accepted records and reports of others including one in a

pole trap on Dava Moor in the 1970s.

Immature male, Greenland race, found dead Pitmain, Kingussie April 1958.

Immature Greenland race seen near Pitmain 24th March 1965.

One Loch Insh 10th May 1972.

One flying south over Cairngorm 14th April 1993.

Peregrine Falcon *Falco peregrinus*
(Scarce resident breeder and migrant)

Over 25 territories in the area but some range over the watershed. Of all British peregrines those in the central Highlands were the least affected by toxic chemicals so the population remained in a reasonable state in the 1960s. Recovered fully in 1970s but some evidence of decline to a lower population in recent years.

A sad history of persecution by game-interests in the past and frequent evidence of stolen eggs and young in the 1970s and 1980s by egg thieves and illegal falconers. Adult males are often at their eyries in winter and the pair are together early in year, e.g. 11th February 1964.

Adults also roost on trees away from nest cliffs in winter. Eggs laid from early April; young fly in June–July and disperse in August–September. Ringed young have been recovered in Galway (520 kilometres SW), New Galloway and Caithness.

Red Grouse *Lagopus lagopus scoticus*
(Common resident breeder)

Common bird of the heather moors and mountain slopes up to 1,000 metres, occasionally higher in late summer when feeding on berries. Numbers highest in the east, although moors bordering Moray affected by ticks and numbers low in early 1980s. Long-term decrease in most areas during recent decades although numbers cyclical. Gathers into flocks in very snowy weather, for example, 250 Slochd 5th February 1963; 1,000 Blackmount 11th February 1988; 350 Strone 28th February 1990.

Ptarmigan *Lagopus mutus*
(Numerous resident breeder)

Widespread above 1,000 metres, sometimes down to 700 metres. Numbers fluctuate in cycles with a run of good years followed by low numbers. Flocks together in autumn and winter; egg-laying from early May in good summers.

Birds can be seen near the ski-lifts and in the past were killed by colliding with cables; breeding success in these areas can be poor. Counts include: 40+ Cairngorm 24th July 1988 and 33 Carn Ban Mor 12th September 1992.

Black Grouse *Lyrurus tetrix*
(Numerous resident breeder, less common in recent decades)

Congregates at traditional lek grounds where males perform elaborate displays. Occasional early morning gatherings from January, regularly late March–early June; some resurgence of activity in October and November. Abundant last century; about 50 males at five leks between Loch Morlich and Inshriach in 1952; on one occasion 50 males at a lek in Rothiemurchus 23 April 1954. Many lek grounds have a long history of occupation but some are deserted as trees grow up and new ones set up when forests are felled.

The species is now less common, partly due to greater forest cover than earlier in the century and probably also to land use changes including abandonment of hill farming in some places.

Still good numbers, mainly on forest/moorland edges where females nest. Counts at leks have shown variations; one Strathspey lek dropped from 20 males to 14 males in 1963 after a severe winter, back to 18–23 males over the five year period 1970–4 but only 10–13 in 1977–80, seven in 1981 and then moved lek with up to five birds in recent years. Twenty-two males at a Loch Laggan lek in 1986 but now down to 12; similar numbers at several other present day leks.

Some leks have suffered from disturbance by early morning bird-watchers – either view from a good distance or get into hides before dawn and leave only when the lekking birds have flown off. Some leks can be viewed from a car but do not get out.

Capercaillie *Tetrao urogallus*
(Numerous to scarce resident breeder)

Became extinct in Scotland about middle of the eighteenth century; re-introduced in first half of nineteenth century, mainly from Swedish stock. Introduced Invereshie in 1875 but unsuccessful. Four seen Rothiemurchus autumn 1890 and hybrid caper cross pheasant shot on 10 November 1890. Pair nested Inverdruie about 1904. Numbers high in the middle of twentieth century but population has now decreased. Present in all pine forests up to 500 metres, especially natural old woodlands. In winter visits isolated stands of pines. Introduced in 1968 to Cluny Castle woods.

Gathers in flocks in winter, mainly feeding in pine trees, some evidence of sexual segregation (flock 27 Dell, Nethy Bridge 19th February 1967 contained 25 males). Starts to display in March, singly or in small groups, quite often on minor forest roads in early mornings and relatively tame. Larger leks occur; 15 males and 20 females at Forest Lodge 16th April 1961; 18 males near Grantown-on-Spey 1977. Eggs laid from late April; hens sit very tight. Males moult in July and August and become extremely elusive; females with broods also difficult to observe. In autumn used to visit oat stubble fields and also open moors where they eat berries. Breeding success very variable; numbers high in 1962 but success low, nine out of 11 hens in six mile walk Forest Lodge in July had no young, one had one chick and one was incubating late clutch of four eggs; in 1968 50% of 80 birds shot in Abernethy were juveniles.

Population has declined markedly since the 1970s, even in the old pine forest strongholds of Strathspey. Forest loss, overgrazing by deer, fox and crow predation, collisions with forest fences, cold wet weather and disturbance all causes of decline. Used to breed commonly around Loch Garten in 1970s now absent. Some evidence of good breeding season in 1994.

This is a difficult bird to see in late spring and summer. There is concern that lekking grounds are being disturbed by early morning bird-watchers. Birds can be seen on tracks through the forest at dawn and dusk; if you see birds while driving, do not get out of the car and frighten them, let them walk or fly away in their own time. A few individual capercaillies become unafraid of humans and will allow close approach, they even attack the observers! Going to see such birds does not interfere with the breeding stock. Alternatively visit the area in autumn or winter when capercaillies can be seen flying through the woods and there is no risk to the nesting birds.

Red-legged Partridge *Alectoris rufa*
(Introduced resident breeder)

Birds were released for hunting in the Advie area in the 1970s and birds of this species or hybrids with Chukar partridges were released in the Newtonmore area from 1981–2. Presently these hybrid birds are found mainly between Newtonmore and Insh, and some of them breed in the wild. Largest flocks: 21 Invertromie 15th October 1986 and 25 Kingussie 9th December 1992. Some have dispersed and arrived in very odd situations including village gardens, Cairngorm car park 12th April 1988 and east Drumochter plateau 14th June 1989.

Grey Partridge *Perdix perdix*
(Scarce resident breeder)

Last century common as far up as Dalwhinnie, less common in 1970s and now decidedly scarce. Found mainly on farmland and edge of marshes. Egg laying through May (clutch 16 at Tulloch on 29th May 1961) but season extended; newly hatched chicks at Dulnain Bridge 26th August 1978. Numbers affected by severe winters of 1961–2 and 1962–3. Peak count: 40 Kingussie 7th March 1989. Population has also decreased due to farming changes; loss of oat crops on many farms and the change to sheep grazing. Bred Tulloch until 1984 and now extinct, where there used to be over a dozen pairs 50 years ago.

Quail *Coturnix coturnix*
(Rare summer visitor – possibly has nested)

Single birds calling; Grantown-on-Spey for week in June 1922, Kincraig 14th May 1971, Broomhill 7th August 1976 and Insh 5–7th July 1977. Adult female killed on road Pityoulish 2nd July 1969, contained large ovaries; one found freshly dead Boat of Garten 7th August 1982.

In 1989 there was an influx with one to two Insh 29th May–26th June, one near Kingussie 15–17th July, one Duthil 1st

June and two calling Easter Cullachy, near Nethy Bridge 21st July
and four on 24th. Single birds at Insh Marshes 1–5th July 1990
and 14th June 1993.

[Reeve's Pheasant] *Syrmaticus reevesi*
(Introduced extinct breeder)

Numbers released Kinveachy Forest 1970; thought to have bred
there in the wild in 1973 when four males and two females were
seen in December. Wandering birds; two males Kincraig
September–December 1971; one male Drumguish 13th April
1972. Now extinct.

Pheasant *Phasianus colchicus*
(Resident breeder; also numbers released annually)

Widespread in agricultural/wooded areas where self-supporting in
low numbers, e.g. two to three pairs breed on Loch Garten reserve
near crofts. Large numbers released annually from Grantown-on-
Spey to Advie, and smaller numbers elsewhere. Most birds seen
are now reared and released rather than wild bred. Insh Marshes
has about 20–25 pairs annually which is a decline since 1980s.

Water Rail *Rallus aquaticus*
(Scarce breeder and migrant)

Mainly summer visitor, late March to October, in small numbers
to low-level marshes; some possibly resident or wintering
migrants. Calling birds regularly heard from marshes between
Dulnain Bridge and Cluny, the main site is Insh Marshes where
maximum 10 singing June 1976 and 11 in 1991, more often four
to six birds; calling continues to early August. Breeding proved at

five marshes, both eggs and young seen. Winter records: one dead
Insh 5th December 1977 and one dead Loch Insh 11th December
1978, had been ringed as a juvenile in Holland two months
earlier. There is a suggestion that the breeding song is more
reminiscent of Scandinavian birds than those further south in the
United Kingdom.

Spotted Crake *Porzana porzana*
(Rare summer visitor; undoubtedly has bred)

Birds calling with their distinctive whiplash calls have been
recorded at Insh Marshes in 14 out of 22 years 1973–94. Best
years have been 1971 (four singing), 1984 (five), 1987 (five to
seven) and 1991 (four to five). Breeding undoubtedly takes place
but nesting is just about impossible to prove without excessive
disturbance.

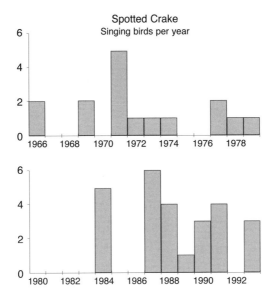

Birds cannot be seen but can be heard from the nearby roads. Single birds have called at three other sites in 1969, 1971 and 1971. Recorded between 29th April and 9th July; mainly for short periods of night time calling. One found dead near Kingussie 29th September 1964 had been prey of short-eared owl.

Corncrake *Crex crex*
(Extinct breeder; vagrant)

Used to be a regular breeder in meadows, no records since 1984. In 1952, breeding was recorded at Tullochgrue (two pairs), Doune and Corrour (one pair Tullochgrue hatched 11 young on 6th July). The species had become very scarce by 1960. After that year, single birds called at Laggan June 1968, Boat of Garten, Ralia and Dulnain Bridge in 1971; Insh 1972 and Grantown-on-Spey 1973. three to four calling Nethy Bridge 2nd August 1977 and at least one same place 25th June and August 1980, when probably bred. Last one calling near Nethy Bridge summer 1984. One found dead Balavil 28th October 1978.

Moorhen *Gallinula chloropus*
(Scarce breeder, rare in winter)

Very small numbers breed on marshes and small lochans; mostly at lower levels, up to 350 metres, throughout the valley. The best place was Insh Marshes where 35–40 pairs in the 1970s but now only three pairs in the 1990s. Similar declines throughout area, so the Moorhen is now a rare visitor in Tulloch; one pair irregularly nests where, there used to be several each spring. Insh decline possibly due to predation by Mink although scarcer after severe winters of 1962 and 1963. Small numbers used to winter most years, especially near Kingussie rubbish dump where up to 10 in

1972 but only four on 18th February 1987; also at Broomhill Bridge 1st January 1973. Usually arrives back on marshes late February – early March, count of 20 Insh Marshes 19th April 1988; later in severe winters. First broods early June; many depart by late September.

Coot *Fulica atra*
(Scarce resident breeder, emigration in severe winters)

Coots used to breed in small numbers on most low level lochs Kingussie to Grantown-on-Spey but there has been a noticeable decline in numbers in last decade. Birds back at nest sites in late March; numbers high in 1970s but lower in 1960s (especially after severe winters) and 1977–82. Estimated 15 pairs Insh Marshes in 1970s to 1976 but only five pairs in 1990s; eggs from late April; flocks in September.

Maximum counts: 60 Loch Insh January and 93 in September 1976, 140 Loch Insh 9th November 1976 and 100 on 20th November 1983; 36 Loch Alvie 1st January 1973; 36 Loch Garten 10th October 1973. Recent peaks only 20 Loch Insh.

Common Crane *Grus grus*
(Vagrant)

One flying NE over Insh Marshes 15th April 1976. One Loch Vaa 14th April 1978. Two at Insh Marshes 3rd–9th May 1987.

A crane, almost certainly this species, Nethy Bridge June–July 1971. Two common cranes escaped from the Highland Wildlife Park in July 1982 and spent the autumn and winter living in the Insh Marshes, they departed on 15th April 1983.

Oystercatcher *Haematopus ostralegus*
(Common summer visitor and breeder)

In the 1890s nested mainly on river shingles as far up as Dalwhinnie; more widespread by middle of this century. Breeds on farmland as well as beside rivers and lochs to the head of the glens, for example, above Gaick at 500 metres. Some suggestions that population has decreased following abandonment of rotational crops on upland farms and through afforestation. 20+ pairs around Laggan in 1970s now less than 10 pairs. Census count of 86 pairs on whole of the Insh Marshes in 1992.

Spring arrivals in first week April in 1890s, now much earlier with first arrivals between 16th and 28th February; earliest one Aviemore 5th February 1967 although 66 at Insh Marshes 16th January 1986 for one day. Birds gather in flocks at regular places in early March before moving to their breeding grounds; 160 Insh Marshes 7th March 1978 and 240 on 13th March 1979. Severe snowstorms in March and April can kill birds which tend not to move back to coasts in bad weather. Pairs on territory early April; individuals faithful to site; eggs from late April; breeding success often poor, less than 5% survived in 1962 and this was probably common place. Departures start in July usually in the evenings; flocks gather before migration, e.g. 175 Insh Marshes 5th August 1980. Migrants leave to the south or south-west (especially from Aviemore to Kingussie) while others fly north to Moray Firth. Most gone by late August but stragglers through September; in 1969, 1973 and 1976 single birds into November, last 23rd. Juveniles ringed in the district have been recovered in SW Scotland (two), NW England (four), Eire (four), S Wales (one) and Jersey (one).

Avocet *Recurvirostra avosetta*
(Vagrant)

A single bird frequented a flooded area beside the Spey at

Broomhill from 18th to 25th April 1984. An influx to northern Scotland was noted in 1984 with an unprecedented count of six at Findhorn Bay in late March.

Ringed Plover *Charadrius hiaticula*
(Scarce summer visitor and breeder)

Small numbers breed on favoured riverine shingle banks of river Spey and tributaries to above Dalwhinnie, also on sandy loch shores from Lochindorb to Loch Laggan. Seven pairs in Newtonmore area, breeding success often poor. Other counts include four pairs Loch Ericht, three pairs Spey Dam and two pairs Loch Pattack. Apparently little or no change since last century, except Loch Morlich where common in 1890s, three to four pairs in 1950s but deserted in 1960s due to disturbance. Species has also ceased to breed on extensive areas of saw dust, left from wartime sawmills, which have now grown over with trees.

Arrives late March, earliest three Insh Marshes 13th March 1974; egg laying late April; emigration in July and August; last record 26th August 1974. Late migrant Loch Insh 5th October 1973. A juvenile ringed at Aviemore 30th June 1955 recovered in Donegal, Eire 4th December 1955 while colour ringing at Newtonmore suggests movement to Moray Firth in winter.

Surprisingly, the species does not breed on the mountain plateaux, but one Carn Ban Mhor (1,170 metres) 3rd August 1966, six Cairn Lochan 31st May 1976 and two near Lochan Buidhe (1,130 metres) 12th June 1979 were considered to be of the northern race, *tundrae*. Further mountain top records in recent years: adult Cairn Lochan 19th May 1987, juvenile same place 24th July 1987; eight Cairngorm 5th June 1988; one Cairn Lochan 16th August 1988.

Dotterel *Charadrius morinellus*
(Scarce to numerous summer visitor and breeder)

This beautiful wader nests on all mountain plateaux above 800 metres; in the last decade numbers have been at the highest levels this century. Dotterel have been studied since the 1950s and for further reading see the species monograph *The Dotterel*.

Arrives in early May (from 30th April), but a very early record on 12th March 1961. Egg-laying from mid-May until late July; breeding success very variable due to weather. Populations on individual plateaux varies with amount of lying snow and birds move between hills, with females laying eggs for males to incubate not only on different hills, but even in Scotland and Norway in the same summer.

Birds flock together in late July and August, several flocks of over 40 recorded in recent years; they then depart with last record on 7th September 1949. Birds winter in North African mountains; for example a local ringing recovery of a juvenile in Algeria on 5th September.

Golden Plover *Charadrius apricarius*
(Numerous summer visitor and breeder)

Breeds over lower moors with reasonable numbers in some areas, for example Dava Moor and the moors on the Moray border where densities of approximately one pair per two square kilometres in the early 1980s. Recent surveys suggest numbers are now lower. In the 1930s, 25–30 pairs bred on the Braes of Abernethy but had decreased to 15–20 pairs in 1950s, with very few now. Also breeds on the grassy mountain plateaux of Badenoch, especially in Western Cairngorms, Grampians and Monadhliaths to 1,170 metres.

Arrives late February and early March, earliest at Insh Marshes 10th February 1980; build up of numbers often on low ground, maximum at Insh Marshes 250 on 8th March 1975. Birds move back and for from grass fields in the valley floor to the moors, even in late May, for example, 61 upper Dulnain river 28th May 1974 (including 20 northern looking birds) and 63 same place 25th April 1990; 90 Nethy Bridge 17th April1986. Egg-laying from late April–early June; flocks gather again in late summer including movements to highest mountain pastures. Twenty-seven Cairn Lochan 5th September 1988 had increased to 100+ by 3rd October. Most depart in August, but some remain into October, last three Insh Marshes 15th November 1981.

Lapwing *Vanellus vanellus*
(Numerous summer visitor and breeder)

Still reasonably widespread breeding species throughout glens on farmland, marshes and close-cropped moorland but clearly much reduced from numbers earlier this century. Plentiful in nineteenth century when abundant central Rothiemurchus June 1891 after forests clear-felled in 1864. Increases in afforestation, abandonment of rotational cropping on upland farms and crofts, cessation of muir burning and sheep grazing on some moors has caused reductions in the breeding population. Also affected in short-term by severe winters. Recent survey Insh Marshes gave 96 pairs in 1992. Has nested on grassy mountain plateaux; two pairs on Carn Ban Mhor (900 metres a.s.l.) in 1939–40.

Spring arrivals start in mid-February, earliest seven Insh Marshes 16–20th January 1976; sometimes arrives in large flocks, 150 Dulnain Bridge 23rd February 1972; numbers increase in March, peaks at Insh Marshes 600 on 14th March 1978; 520 on 8th March 1979 although numbers now lower, 250 on 23rd

February 1990. Other peak counts include 250 Dulnain Bridge 10th March 1986 and 300 Strone 20th February 1993. Disperses to breeding grounds and displays in March and April. Egg-laying from mid-April.

Gathers into flocks late June and departures from July, often in SW direction. One hundred and seventy-five at Insh Marshes 10th July 1979; 70 flew SW Kingussie 21st July 1972 and 105 flew SW Broomhill 12th July 1972. Occasionally in high mountains, one Ben Macdhui (1,250 metres) 4th June 1971. Most gone by September, few in October–December, but occasional flocks pass through valley, for example, 92 Insh 9th October 1979, 36 Boat of Garten 13th November 1962 and 50 Insh 24th December 1979. Ringed juveniles have been recovered in Dundee, Fort William and also back at Nethy Bridge as a four year-old.

Knot *Calidris canutus*
(Vagrant)

One shot Dunachton September 1921; the remains of an adult killed by a Peregrine near Carrbridge May–June 1963; a small flock heard migrating over Aviemore at night July 1973.

Sanderling *Calidris alba*
(Vagrant)

Two in summer plumage were seen in display flight over Carn Ban Mor on 9th June 1974, absent the next day. Also an undated record of the remains of dead sanderling in a Peregrine eyrie.

Temminck's Stint *Calidris temminckii*
(Extinct rare breeder and rare migrant)

A pair with four eggs was found at Loch Morlich on 13th June 1934 but the clutch was deserted; a pair was also present in 1935 and a female with four eggs in 1936, one bird in 1947 and a pair with a nest in 1956 but none were successful. In 1974, two birds seen at another site; at least five were present the following year and breeding probably occurred. This site was occupied for a further 11 years but no birds have been observed there since 1986. Hatched young were seen in at least six of the years. Single migrants near Boat of Garten 22nd May 1974, 30th May 1979 and 3rd July 1982; Loch Insh 15th July 1989.

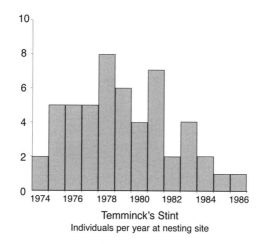

Temminck's Stint
Individuals per year at nesting site

Purple Sandpiper *Calidris maritima*
(Rare sporadic breeder)

Single pairs nested in 1985 and 1989, and a single was seen in another locality in 1989.

Dunlin *Calidris alpina*
(Scarce summer visitor and breeder)

Small numbers breed on the wettest parts of Dava Moor; on

grassier mountain plateaux of the West Cairngorms and
Grampians and the Monadhliaths; also nests beside a few lochs in
Badenoch. Dunlins used to nest beside Loch Morlich, one to two
pairs in 1950s. Arrives early May and departs July–early August.

Unusual migrants include one Insh Marshes 29th
January–2nd February 1976, one Loch Insh 3rd November 1983
and 30+ south over Insh Marshes 8th October 1988.

Ruff *Philomachus pugnax*
(Vagrant)

Only two records in spring and summer:
Male in breeding plumage near Kingussie 7th May 1967.
One Newtonmore 19th July 1971.

Jack Snipe *Lymnocryptes minimus*
(Rare winter visitor)

Single birds Kincardine 20th October 1894, Badenoch and
Kincraig 11th and 27th October 1896. Single birds Kincraig 1st
February 1971, and Pitmain mid-December 1976. Single birds on
nine occasions Insh Marshes 1973–94 between 29th September
and 31st December but also one on the unusual date of 10th
May 1991. Scattered records elsewhere in area, for example: two
Inverlaidnan December 1982; single birds Aberarder 10th
October 1987, Abernethy 1st January 1989 and several since; one
Tulloch 12th November 1994.

Snipe *Capella gallinago*
(Numerous breeder and migrant)

Widespread but thinly spread breeder throughout district; well up glens to 500 metres a.s.l., but highest numbers nest in the low ground marshes. For example, 55–80 pairs estimated Insh Marshes 1976 while a 1992 census gave 135 pairs on the reserve and a total of 228 territories on whole Insh Marshes SSSI area. Also in boggy areas of moorlands, forest bogs, lochans etc. Noticeable increase observed in Rothiemurchus late 1940s–early 1950s. Arrives late February–early March, display from 4th March. Less seen after September, further departures October–November, some in winter and almost certainly some immigration.

Great Snipe *Capella media*
(Vagrant)

Two old records of this difficult to observe species:
One shot Glenshirra September 1884.
One found dead by river Spey near Dulnain Bridge 20th August 1934.

Woodcock *Scolopax rusticolus*
(Numerous breeder and migrant)

Well distributed in all open wooded areas, especially in birch woods. Spring arrival of breeders occurs in late February with first dates of display early March (earliest 22nd February 1986). Roding flights are a frequent sight in spring and early summer evenings, especially over birch woods and forest edges. The numbers nesting are difficult to estimate; one census gave 10 territories around Insh Marshes in 1992. First eggs recorded 29th March; long nesting season with day old chicks seen Loch Garten 25th July 1962. Departures August to October. It is believed our woodcock winter in Ireland while Scandinavian migrants arrive in early November, with small numbers wintering.

Black-tailed Godwit *Limosa limosa*
(Scarce spring visitor)

Small numbers have occurred in spring from the first record at
Loch Insh 29th June 1960. All spring migrants carefully checked
have been of the Icelandic race and have occurred between 5th
April and 29th June. Insh Marshes is the main site, with records
of one to two birds in 11 springs between 1973 and 1994, and
annual since 1986. There was a flock of 26 on 28th April 1994
with 10 still present on 30th. Three summered Insh Marshes in
1964 with Single birds in 1965 and 1970; single pairs have
displayed on single dates in two recent springs but there has been
no evidence of breeding. Other records include: single birds Boat
of Garten 12–13th June 1962, 18th June 1974 and four there
23rd April 1990; three Spey Dam 5th May 1984.

Bar-tailed Godwit *Limosa lapponica*
(Vagrant)

Only three records of this common winter visitor to the Moray
Firth:
Heard migrating over Aviemore at night July 1973.
One Tulloch moor 16th April 1975.
Heard migrating at night Cat Lodge 21–2nd May 1989.

Whimbrel *Numenius phaeopus*
(Extinct rare breeder; scarce migrant)

A pair reported nesting near Newtonmore 1924. A pair nested
there successfully in 1931, two pairs in 1932 (one infertile) and
one pair 1933 (probably one to two pairs cup to 1938). One
migrant Alvie 4th August 1889; two Loch Garten 22nd May 1961.

Recorded as a migrant in very small numbers most years 1968–94 between 9th April and 17th June and 15th July–22nd August. Peak counts include: six Loch Garten 28th April 1977 and three on 11th August 1980; 12 Tulloch Moor 9th April 1986. One in the mountains at Lurcher's Gully 12th June 1991.

Curlew *Numenius arquata*
(Common summer visitor and breeder; rare winter migrant)

Breeds in good numbers throughout the district in marshes, wet farmland, wetter moorland, forest bogs and clearings. Estimates include 25–30 pairs at Insh Marshes in 1970s but survey over larger reserve area in 1992 gave 80 pairs with 129 pairs on whole Insh Marshes SSSI. Arrives in late February and early March (earliest 9th February 1992), numbers build up on lower ground in March, maximum 120 Insh Marshes 17th March 1981 and 150+ on 2nd April 1983. Display at breeding grounds from 9th March; young are often brought into hay fields when old enough to walk.

Gathers in flocks in late June and July with departures often to the south-west, for example, 17 flew south Loch Garten 25th July 1972. Very few remain by mid-August although six W over Tulloch on 14th September 1994.

Stragglers occur in the autumn and winter, including single birds in November (two), December (two) and January. Ringed juveniles have been recovered in Co. Galway (31st July, ringed in June), Co. Kerry (February), Islay (April) and Dufftown (27th July). Also a Norwegian juvenile found long dead at the Slochd 10th April 1969.

Spotted Redshank *Tringa erythropus*
(Rare migrant)

Eight records of 10 birds. Birds giving brief displays in Rothiemurchus 1956, two at Spey Dam 31st May 1977 and one Loch Garten May 1979. Single birds in spring at Insh Marshes 16–19th April 1973, 22nd April 1974 and 29th April–2nd May 1992. Autumn migrants: Loch Garten 29th August 1972 and two Insh Marshes 20th August 1983.

Redshank *Tringa totanus*
(Numerous summer visitor and breeder)

Breeds in reasonable numbers in various marshes and marshy lochs throughout area, main haunt in marshes by river Spey. Recorded as common Insh Marshes 1890s; 21–26 pairs estimated in 1976 but 1992 survey gave 105 pairs on larger reserve with 159 pairs on Insh Marshes SSSI. A decrease since the 1960s through drainage of wet fields on farms.

Arrives in March (earliest 2nd March 1976), mainly late March; display from 23rd. Gathers in flocks after breeding, 36 Insh Marshes 19th July 1976, emigration in late June–July; migrating SW through Drumochter in July; two flew south over Lurcher's Meadow at 1,000 metres altitude 3rd August 1990. Last records 28th August but later single migrant 8th October 1979 at Insh Marshes. Local juveniles recovered in Dumfries, Alnwick and Caithness (April).

Greenshank *Tringa nebularia*
(Scarce summer visitor and breeder)

Breeds in very small numbers, principally in the glens of Badenoch up to 700 metres, with even smaller numbers, three to five pairs in Strathspey. Has disappeared from various areas because of habitat changes; abundant around Loch Morlich on

16th May 1962, also present Dalwhinnie and Laggan where there were none in 1860s. There were about 11 pairs Loch Morlich to Inshriach in 1930s, five to six pairs Morlich area 1953 and still six pairs there in 1962 but removal of sheep, increase of afforestation and tourism has resulted in desertion of that area.

Similarly there used to be four pairs in the Braes of Abernethy until early 1960s but now only occurs further into the glen. The species undoubtedly benefited from forest removal, burning and heavy grazing by domestic stock in past centuries but has now withdrawn as forest has returned, especially in Strathspey.

Arrives in late March and April (earliest 17th); chicks from late May; departs June–early August, stragglers to early September; last dates 10th and 18th October. Irregular migrant at Insh Marshes between 3rd April and 15th September, with less in recent years.

Green Sandpiper *Tringa ochropus*
(Extinct breeder, scarce migrant)

The only breeding record for Scotland of this boreal forest species was a pair seen with one chick near Loch an Eilein on 29th May 1959. One to two were seen there in 1960 and one in 1961. Other summering records are a male displaying between Inshriach and Rothiemurchus in the summer of 1933–34, a pair there in 1935, a male each summer 1936–41, a pair 1942 and 1948, and one late summer 1950.

Migrants: one Avielochan 23rd April 1961. Since 1971 has occurred on passage 21st April–19th August, about 20 birds in April (two), May (five), June, July & August (13); all single birds except three Loch Garten 29th July 1980 and two Insh Marshes 20th August 1983. Late single Kinchurdy 14th September.

Wood Sandpiper *Tringa glareola*
(Rare summer visitor and breeder)

Very small numbers breed nearly annually in the district but sites
may be deserted for years. Before nesting started in 1968 the
following migrants were recorded: single birds Loch Insh 18th
May 1940, Newtonmore 5th June 1950, Loch Insh 28th May
1959, Avielochan 26th May 1961 and Tulloch moor 17th June
1961.

From 1968 has nested, often successfully, most years, with
peaks of four to six pairs in 1968 and five to seven pairs in 1980
at original site, less in recent years. Bred at another site from
1983–94, with up to two to three pairs in best years. Has also
occurred at two or three other potential nesting sites with
occasional migrants elsewhere in area. Arrives from 4th May,
present to late July; last 11th August. This is a sensitive and rare
breeding species; displaying birds are visible but nest sites should
not be approached.

Common Sandpiper *Actitis hypoleucos*
(Numerous summer visitor and breeder)

Breeds beside all rivers and many lochs, even high into the hill
glens throughout the district; one pair nests Loch Cnapan (900
metres a.s.l.). Numbers high in many areas: 45 pairs on river Spey
between Kincraig and Boat of Garten 1–3rd May 1961; 25 pairs
Rothiemurchus and Loch Morlich 1953 but has now decreased at
Morlich. Recent survey Insh Marshes SSSI revealed 26 pairs in
1992. Spring arrivals usually late April, earliest Loch Garten 3rd
April 1972 and Insh Marshes 12th April. Often a day or two
earlier at Loch Garten than at Insh. Egg-laying from early May;
gather in small flocks in early July, for example 54 Insh Marshes

7th July 1980, 57 on 10th July 1979. Departs July and August, often at night, last records to 27th August. Late migrants Loch Garten 10th September 1981 and Insh Marshes 2nd October 1976.

Turnstone *Arenaria interpres*
(Vagrant)

Only three records of this common winter visitor to the Moray Firth:
One Loch Insh 8th August 1978.
One Loch Insh 14th June 1982.
One Lochindorb 15th May 1985.

Red-necked Phalarope *Phalaropus lobatus*
(Extinct summer visitor and breeder)

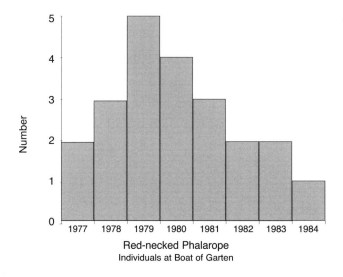

Red-necked Phalarope
Individuals at Boat of Garten

A pair nested Loch Insh 6th June 1914, with only one adult 1916. One reported at Loch Morlich summer 1954. One Spey Dam 11th June 1981. In 1977 a pair were found near Boat of

Garten on 7th June, a nest of four eggs was found on 28th June and hatched on 5th July, female seen to 30th July. Birds returned to this site for the following seven years with the following numbers seen: 1978 (three), 1979 (four to five), 1980 (four), 1981 (three), 1982 (two), 1983 (two) but only a single female in 1984 and none seen since. Breeding was believed to have occurred in most years.

Pomarine Skua *Stercorarius pomarinus*
(Vagrant)

Two records in 1985, possibly relating to the same individual: One dark-phase adult flying south over Insh Marshes 28th April 1985. One at Boat of Garten 30th April 1985.

Arctic Skua *Stercorarius parasiticus*
(Rare migrant)

Eight records of single birds since 1971; five in May and three in autumn. Single birds Cairngorm 31st May 1971, Loch Morlich 14th September 1974 and Kingussie 30th September 1978; Insh Marshes 7th May 1982, 25th May 1986 and 20th May 1987; Loch Mallachie 12th November 1982; flying north Dalwhinnie 28th May 1984.

Long-tailed Skua *Stercorarius longicaudus*
(Vagrant)

Three records of adults in June of this tundra breeding species:
Adult Drumochter hills (a ringed bird) 18th June 1974.
Adult found freshly killed by car on the road from Grantown-on-Spey to Bridge of Brown 4th June 1975.

Adult over Carn Ban Mor 16th June 1984.
(Also two possibles over Cairn Lochan on 18th June 1988. A flock of 20 small skuas flew low NE over Loch Garten 24th May 1966, may have been this species.)

Great Skua *Stercorarius skua*
(Vagrant)

Three records since 1975; two in spring and one in autumn:
One Loch Garten 22nd April 1975.
One Glen Feshie 26th April 1979.
One Kingussie 16th September 1983.

Little Gull *Larus minutus*
(Vagrant)

Only one record: immature Insh Marshes 15–18th May 1975.

Sabine's Gull *Larus sabini*
(Vagrant)

Only one record; immature Loch Insh 8th September 1975.

Black-headed Gull *Larus ridibundus*
(Common breeder and summer visitor)

Nests at colonies, very variable in size, throughout the district; some traditional colonies very old, others have been deserted while some new colonies have been recently started. In general the species is now less common, probably due to changes in agriculture, especially abandonment of rotational cropping and decrease in spring ploughing. One local farmer ploughing in

Tulloch 4th April 1994 commented that no gulls followed the tractor whereas as hundreds used to.

Large colony Abernethy 1890s now deserted; very old colony Tulloch Moor, up to 200 pairs in 1950s and 1960s, deserted in 1970s; big colonies Pityoulish and Dalfaber no longer used; Kinrara 13 pairs in 1891, about 400 pairs in 1980s, now less; Insh Marshes colony known in 1890s, now largest colony in district, 2,000–2,500 pairs in several sites 1979–1980s but now more like 12–1500 pairs (some suggestions that numbers may have been as high as 10,000 pairs in the middle of this century. New colony 550 pairs Kinchurdy in late 1980s–1990. Smaller colonies various other areas, also few pairs attempted to breed in 1958 at Loch an Stuirteag, 900 metres a.s.l. in mountains near Cairntoul.

Birds arrive in spring flying up river from Grantown-on-Spey; first dates between 16th February 1980 (27) and 11th March, numbers build up in March and visit colonies in day time. Roosts communally at night at larger lochs in April; 4,000 Loch Insh in 1975; peaks at Loch Garten of 6,000 on 11th April 1972 and 6,000 on 6th April 1973, lower in recent years, maximum 3,500 on 9th April 1980 and 4,500 on 5th April 1987. Flying young from mid-June and most colonies deserted by end July; occasionally visits high tops, for example, 120 Cairn Lochan plateau 25th July 1979. Few remain into September, stragglers to November usually sickly birds but occasional migrants: 19 Avielochan 14th October 1972, four Loch Insh 18th December 1977, two Aviemore 18th January 1982. One Norwegian juvenile recovered, two months after ringing, at Nethy Bridge 15th August 1976.

Common Gull *Larus canus*
(Numerous breeder, mainly in west)

Breeds on moorland lochs and river shingles rather than marshes. Some breed Dorback and Dava but mostly west of Kingussie, 100–300 pairs Spey Dam, 150 pairs in 1989, 50 pairs Loch Spey (1974); some tree nests Loch Gynack 1969; small regular colony (six pairs) Loch an Stuirteag (900 metres a.s.l.) near Cairntoul also three pairs on edge of Black-headed Gull colony at Insh Marshes.

Regularly arrives in early March, earliest 12th February 1962; count of 120 on Loch Insh March 1991; departs July–August. Sometimes seen hawking high tops for insects in summer, also more often seen in Strathspey in July and August. Stragglers September–January, tend to be weakly immatures.

Lesser Black-backed Gull *Larus fuscus*
(Numerous summer visitor; has bred in past)

Recorded breeding Abernethy peat mosses 1890s, no recent records. Arrives in late March and April (earliest Aviemore 8th March 1977), small numbers throughout summer, maximum 30

Aviemore refuse tip 10th June 1994; 20 Loch Garten 21st August, stragglers to 24th September.

Migrates over to south and south-west July–September, for example, 10 flew S Loch Insh 31st August. One Loch Garten 25th January 1987. Two records of Scandinavian race: one Pityoulish 15th April 1963, two Cairn Lochan 24th June 1977.

Herring Gull *Larus argentatus*
(Rare breeder; common visitor and migrant)

Pair nested Spey Dam 1982 and still just one pair in 1986. Seen throughout year, mainly in winter scavenging at Aviemore refuse tip and roosting at Loch Garten. Inland roost at Loch Garten varies from year to year, peak numbers 120 on 27th February 1962, 96 on 31st December 1972, 350 on 6th April 1973, 256 on 6th March 1977, 450 on 13th September 1986 and 30th September 1987. Used to visit dumps at Kingussie, Newtonmore and Grantown-on-Spey but they are now closed. At Loch Insh roost peak numbers, 100 in March 1973 and 230 on 23rd February 1977; but recent peak of only 70 in November 1992. Grantown-on-Spey feeders used to roost flight at dusk each day to the Moray Firth.

Passage most evident in July and August, when families pass over south and south-west, sometimes with squeaking juveniles following adults; for example, 15 flew SW over Aviemore 9th August 1973. Juvenile ringed at Eathie, Ross-shire 1968 recovered Cromdale March 1977; full-grown bird ringed at Bishopriggs December 1978 recovered Aviemore February 1980. A yellow-legged Herring Gull on river Spey 15th August 1993.

Iceland Gull *Larus glaucoides*
(Rare winter visitor)

Six individuals between December and January since 1984:
Adult Balavil 10th December 1984.
One Loch Garten 10–14th April 1988, same bird Aviemore tip
15th April 1988.
One Loch Garten 12th January 1993, two on 28th January 1993.
Adult Loch Insh 26th February 1994.
One Loch Garten March 1994.

Glaucous Gull *Larus hyperboreus*
(Rare winter visitor)

Eight single birds in January to June, since first in 1983:
Adult Loch Insh 13th March 1983.
Adult Loch Garten 10th January 1984.
Immature Loch Garten 8th April 1989.
Adult Loch Alvie 5–6th May 1990 and at Loch Insh 6th May 1990.
Second-year bird Invertromie 5th June 1991.
Second-winter bird Loch Insh 9th March 1991.
One Insh Marshes 13th–15th January 1993.
One Loch Garten January and February 1993.

Great Black-backed Gull *Larus marinus*
(Rare breeder; numerous visitor)

A pair nested on the island at Spey Dam in 1986 and continued
to do so until 1990, three seen in 1989. Birds are seen
throughout the year, most November to April; adults and
immatures scavenging on rubbish dumps and on dead salmon
along the rivers. Inland roost at Loch Garten; peak counts 60 on
27th February 1962, 112 on 31st December 1972, 60 on 6th
April 1973, 223 on 10th December 1978 and 140 on 31st
December 1994.

Birds which used to feed at Grantown-on-Spey dump in the 1960s roosted at night on the Moray Firth. Migrants have been observed flying south and south-west in July, for example, 18th July 1971.

Kittiwake *Rissa tridactyla*
(Scarce passage migrant)

Evidence of a cross-country spring migration route from the head of Loch Linnhe (Fort William) where flocks occur in late March and April to the Moray Firth, main route is via Loch Ness. Peak counts: 440 Loch Laggan 1st April 1962; 80+ Insh Marshes 24th January 1973; three Loch Garten 14th March 1981; 104 Loch Insh 9th April 1987, four there on 18th January 1993 and and 25 on 4th April 1993. At least 20 other records of single birds from Aviemore to Broomhill between October and May; one Cairngorm 20th July 1980.

Sandwich Tern *Sterna sandvicensis*
(Vagrant)

Two records of migrants passing overland:
One between Dalwhinnie and Drumochter 15th July 1967.
One Loch Insh 18th August 1976.

Common Tern *Sterna hirundo*
(Scarce summer visitor and breeder)

In 1890s nested in small numbers on river shingles Kingussie and on Dulnain river above Carrbridge; distribution similarly widespread and numbers still very small, possibly a maximum of 10–15 pairs in the district.

Recorded 5th May to 4th August, maximum count of 10 at Loch Insh 4th August 1979 and 15 on 9th July 1990.

Black Tern *Chlidonias niger*
(Vagrant)

Four records involving seven individuals:
One Loch Morlich 18th August 1962.
One Loch Insh 10th May 1969.
Four Loch Morlich 7th September 1978.
One Kinchurdy 19th April 1987.

Guillemot *Uria aalge*
(Vagrant)

Four records since 1987, found stranded in autumn and released on coast:
One Loch Insh 14th September 1987.
One Kincraig 19th September 1989.
One Grantown-on-Spey 19th September 1989.
One Kincraig 25th September 1989.

Little Auk *Alle alle*
(Vagrant)

Four records of storm driven birds, only one in recent years:
One found dead or dying after storms Grantown-on-Spey 19th January 1895.
One found dead or dying Kingussie 20th January 1895.
One found dead Newtonmore January 1916.
One found exhausted Kingussie 13th January 1993, died overnight.

Puffin *Fratercula arctica*
(Vagrant)

Three records of lost birds:
One found dead in Peregrine eyrie near Laggan late June 1968.
One Invereshie 20th April 1967, released on Loch Insh.
One very weak bird Loch Laggan 26th April 1990.

Pallas's Sand Grouse *Syrrhaptes paradoxus*
(Vagrant)

Recorded during the famous invasion years of 1863 and 1888; in latter year was seen at Grantown-on-Spey and Kincraig while two were shot at East Croftmore, Boat of Garten.

Feral Pigeon *Columba livia*
(Scarce resident breeder and migrant)

Small numbers occur on farms where they nest in buildings; occasionally single pairs breed in isolated derelict buildings. Birds pass over, especially in pigeon racing season.

Stock Dove *Columba oenas*
(Rare migrant breeder)

Nowadays this is a rare or nearly extinct breeder in Strathspey, with records in the last five years only from Coylumbridge and Pityoulish, four on 19th June 1989, pair 5th May 1994, with no recent proof of breeding.

Last record in Badenoch at Insh Marshes 18th April 1986. Recorded at Kincraig in 1889 but breeding not proved; recorded Rothiemurchus, Nethy Bridge and Dorback in early 1950s.

Nested Cat's Den Rothiemurchus 1961–3 and a few Pityoulish 1961–2.

Recorded Aviemore-Boat of Garten in 1969; three Alvie 2nd December 1973; no records until 1978 when two Alvie, two Kingussie, two Tulloch and one Pityoulish, so numbers variable but very small. Pair Creag Dubh, Newtonmore 19th April 1979.

Wood Pigeon *Columba palumbus*
(Numerous breeder; many depart for winter)

Abundant in 1890s; increased in early 1960s, less from 1970s to present time. Breeds in woods throughout district; flocks in autumn. Maximum counts: 300 Insh Marshes 21st February–23rd March 1980 and 242 Tulloch 30th March 1980; recently 86 Carrbridge 11th March 1991 and 84 Broomhill 1st March 1992. Early nesting in mild winters, two nests with eggs Nethy Bridge 4–5th February 1962.

Collared Dove *Streptopelia decaocto*
(Scarce to numerous resident breeder, scarce migrant)

One Dell Hotel, Rothiemurchus 2nd July 1961 was first for Inverness-shire. Single birds Kingussie 1st March 1967 and Nethy Bridge 24th December 1967. First bred 1968, two pairs Nethy Bridge and two pairs Kincraig; in 1969 breeding or probable breeding Laggan, Dalwhinnie, Kingussie, Kincraig, Boat of Garten and Nethy Bridge; further increase in numbers and localities throughout 1970s and early 1980s. Then levelled out and now definitely decreased in numbers.

Migrants at Insh Marshes have also shown a similar decline dating back to 1979. A bird ringed in Cheshire was seen in Badenoch 10th July 1969.

Turtle Dove *Streptopelia turtur*
(Rare summer migrant)

First record at Tulloch 7th June 1967, then single birds
Auchgourish 8th June and Rothiemurchus 1st September 1967.
Recorded in all but four years between 1968 and 1981; 13
sightings, usually only on one day, mainly 13th May–28th June,
one 24th August. All single birds except two on 28th June 1978
at Coylumbridge. Since then has become rare with only three
records in last ten years; single birds Rothiemurchus 8–10th June
1985, Glenmore 14th July 1989 and Loch Vaa 11th May 1990.

Cuckoo *Cuculus canorus*
(Numerous summer visitor and breeder)

Cuckoos breed throughout the district, up to 700 metres a.s.l. on
moorlands as well as near forest edges and scattered woodland.
Arrives late April: first dates 11th April 1976 Glenfeshie; 14th
(1985), 19th (1994), 24th (four years), 27th (four years) and
29th (four years). Birds late in 1979 (6th May) and 1981 (3rd
May). Most of the females parasitise meadow and tree pipits.
Most departed by end July, juveniles to mid-August, last records
24th August 1973 and Insh 4th September 1979.

Barn Owl *Tyto alba*
(Rare visitor or resident)

No records of breeding but may have done so on a very rare
occasion. Single birds Coylumbridge and near Aviemore 1952,
Rothiemurchus June 1953, Kincraig 1968, Dulnain Bridge 1971,
Newtonmore 4–20th November 1971, Balavil 5th February 1975,
Dalraddy 17th–26th May (calling), Kingussie 11th December

1982, Loch Insh 3–9th December 1986, one Loch Laggan 27th February 1988, Kinveachy 27th October 1990, Inshriach 21st November 1991 and one attracted by calling captive Barn Owls at Laggan March–April 1990.

Snowy Owl *Nyctea scandiaca*
(Rare visitor)

Three reported in Glen Feshie 1st May 1927. Probably at least five, probably six individuals have occurred on the Cairngorm-Macdhui plateaux during various summers from 1952–92, these birds are usually just over the county march in Grampian Region but are occasionally seen on this side of the watershed. A male in June 1952 and 19th July–13th September 1953 ranged as far as Sgoran Dubh. A male occurred in summer 1963 and 1964 (5th June), 1965 (23rd April–17th October, with a different bird on 8th August) and 1966 (25th June–3rd July). A male in 1979 (25th July–15th September), 1980 (27th July–31st August) and 1981 (2nd April). Male in 1984 (21st June– 1st October) was seen at Carn Ban Mor on 10th November. Female at Cairngorm 11st August–4th September 1987; female Cairngorms July 1989, 28th May–3rd August 1990, 15th April 1991 and June–September 1992.

Tawny Owl *Strix aluco*
(Common resident breeder)

Widespread but thinly distributed throughout valley to tree limit, rarely seen higher than 400 metres a.s.l.. Eggs laid from late March; has nested in nest boxes, hollow trees and old nests. Population hit by severe winters such as 1961–2, 1962–3 and 1981–2; three found dead in snow Tulloch 1–3rd January 1962. A juvenile ringed near Loch Morlich found dead near Kincraig in November.

Long-eared Owl *Asio otus*
(Scarce resident breeder)

Irregular in numbers throughout forested areas, sometimes in isolated plantations. Recorded throughout whole area but numbers variable.

In 1890s recorded in fair numbers up to Newtonmore but very rare Rothiemurchus-Abernethy 1934–52. Thereafter an increase and quite plentiful Abernethy 1960–1 when four to six pairs in woods near Loch Garten; three broods of young seen on 10th May, 16th May and 14th June 1960. Many died in severe winters of 1961–2 and 1962–3; Abernethy breeders in 1962 down to one third. Rather scarce mid 1970s but more in 1980s, although seems scarcer in 1990s. Display and calling January–March, eggs late March–April. Most likely to be seen and heard when broods make squeaking contact calls in May and June. Recoveries of ringed juveniles within 30 kilometres of nests.

Short-eared Owl *Asio flammeus*
(Rare or scarce breeder and migrant)

Very few pairs have nested in the district in recent years; in good vole years a few pairs can be found on moors, but definitely rarer now than in past.

Pairs used to breed irregularly spaced on lower moors and foothills, also sometimes in larger forest clearings, new conifer plantations and marshes. Population high in 1960 (seven pairs Tulloch, Dorback and at Carrbridge, one nest with six young) when many voles for food; numbers still high in 1961 but very scarce in 1962 after severe winter and shortage of voles.

Can be rare as breeder for a run of years. Numbers higher again 1979–81 and more successful. One to two pairs nest in good vole years at Insh Marshes last peak count six in July 1981. Eggs in April, young in May. One hunting high mountain plateau Cairn Lochan July 1972.

Nightjar *Caprimulgus europaeus*
(Rare summer visitor; used to breed)

Recorded as a familiar bird in Badenoch in 1792. Present 1890s when eggs were collected Abernethy. Pair Rothiemurchus 1948, male Coylumbridge 1951 and 1952; pair Inshriach 1961. Singing birds Inshriach 1971, Loch Garten 3rd July 1973, Boat of Garten 27th May 1976 and Tulloch 27th July 1980. Two recent records: Tulloch 21st August 1993 and Loch Garten 9th August 1994.

Swift *Apus apus*
(Numerous summer visitor and breeder)

Common in villages, such as Boat of Garten and Newtonmore, where the screaming of Swifts is a feature of the summer scene; also nests in isolated houses. Since 1983 increasing use of old woodpecker nest holes for nesting, mainly Abernethy where at least three in use in 1986; also uses nest box on tree in Tulloch. Change may be due to decrease of available nesting sites in villages as old houses are renovated to modern standards and new houses have no nest cavities. Could also be a decline in breeding population.

Spring arrivals in May, usually first dates 11–18th May, but one over Insh 2nd May 1980 and four Nethy Bridge 5th May. Gathers in large numbers over Insh Marshes and Loch Morlich in

summer, presumably gathering food for young; 500+ Insh 2nd
August 1973 and 1,000 on 5th August 1974, but numbers not
over 200 since 1977; 100 Loch Morlich 7th July 1972.

In fine weather sometimes visits high tops, 35 Cairngorm
12th June 1992. Last records; 40+ Grantown-on-Spey 9th
September 1992; single birds Aviemore 17th September 1923,
Insh 18th September 1978 and Boat of Garten 22nd September
1977; two Aviemore 1st October and one 12th November.

Alpine Swift *Apus melba*
(Vagrant)

One over Boat of Garten with Swifts on 24th July 1989.

Kingfisher *Alcedo atthis*
(Rare breeder and visitor)

Only four records to 1984: Newtonmore 16–30th November
1952, Dalfaber, Aviemore 11th November 1982, Kincraig 28th
October 1982 and Kinchurdy 27th September 1983.Then an
increase of sightings from one at Pityoulish on 15th September
1987. In 1988 single birds at Insh Marshes in April and August
to December, with a party of five together on the river Spey at
the Doune in July suggesting local breeding.

Singles at Kingussie 6th February and November–December
1989 and single birds at Broomhill mid July and Boat of Garten
mid July 1989. Single birds seen at Kingussie in October 1990
and Broomhill in November 1991. In 1992 single birds seen
regularly at Broomhill and one seen entering hole in sand martin
colony in river bank, also single seen Carrbridge in March. In
1993 pair nested at Broomhill, but river bank swept away in flood
during incubation; two seen Aviemore on 28th May, Kincraig

August, Feshiebridge September and probably two birds Insh Marshes May to August. One in 1994 near Feshiebridge flying into river bank.

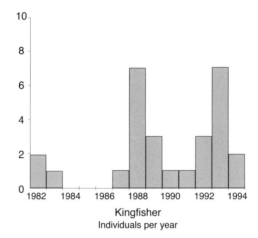

Kingfisher
Individuals per year

Roller *Coracias garrulus*
(Vagrant)

One shot Abernethy Forest prior to 1892.

Hoopoe *Upupa epops*
(Vagrant)

Six records over a period of 17 years from 1972: One at Achlean 7th June 1972. One Rothiemurchus 9–11th May 1973. One Speybank, near Kincraig 5th May 1983. One at Nethy Bridge 6th November 1986. One Dalchully 8–9th October and at Crathie on 11th October 1988. One Insh 29th October 1988.

Wryneck *Jynx torquilla*
(Rare irregular breeder, rare summer visitor)

First record one shot The Dell, Nethy Bridge 4th June 1919; next

Glenmore 25–26th May 1952; Single birds in 1954, 1961 (twice), 1962 and 1965. Three birds including a pair recorded in 1968, followed by at least three pairs nesting in 1969 (first for Scotland). Since then birds have nested in forests and scattered woodlands on occasions in various years 1977–93; also records of passage birds and short-term visitors between 26th April and 29th July.

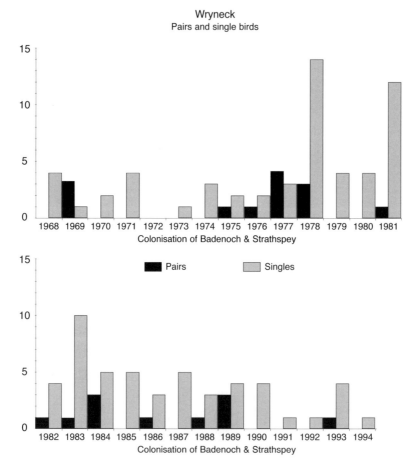

Wryneck
Pairs and single birds

Colonisation of Badenoch & Strathspey

Colonisation of Badenoch & Strathspey

Birds recorded annually from 1977–94, with breeding confirmed in nine years, usually just a single pair, with some evidence of pairs returning to same nest for several seasons.

Green Woodpecker *Picus viridus*
(Rare resident breeder)

Unconfirmed reports of birds in 1960s but first accepted records
were one or two Doune-Kinrara 7th February–26th March 1971.
These were considered to be colonists from Perthshire. There was
one Kingussie 1973, two Feshiebridge, one Insh and one
Glenmore in 1974, one Insh in 1975 and an increase in 1976.

First juveniles were seen in 1978 when birds were present in six to eight areas. Increase continued and recorded in 13 areas in 1981 between Newtonmore and Nethy Bridge with breeding at several sites. At least seven to ten sites with birds during 1980s with colonization of new areas; first breeding at Insh in 1992. Still present in early part of 1994 with numbers lower, but a big crash in latter half of the year, and species is now absent from most former sites.

Great Spotted Woodpecker *Dendrocopus major*
(Scarce to numerous resident breeder)

Present in Strathspey in 1830 but became scarcer with forest clearances and might have become extinct, as in rest of Scotland, at this time. A few pairs in Abernethy Forest 1878 to 1890 suggest that a very small pocket of survivors remained in the ancient pine forest. Increased since turn of century; bred Aviemore 1920. Now well distributed throughout all wooded areas of the district but not a common bird and may have declined in last decade. Census gave four pairs on Insh Marshes reserve; highest count seven in July 1977. Young very noisy at nest hole before fledgling in June. Occasionally visits bird tables in winter; numbers low after severe winter of 1962–3.

Skylark *Alauda arvensis*
(Common breeder, mainly absent in autumn and winter)

Breeds throughout the district although numbers are much reduced now compared to 1950s and 60s when species increased noticeably on moorlands and then colonised high grassy plateaux. Found nesting on Cairngorm and Carn Ban Mhor in early 1960s at over 1,000 metres a.s.l.. Arrives back very early in year, depending on snow cover. Usually first records between 1–20th February, mainly late February and March when 800 Laggan 5th March 1962. Late snows often forced birds onto snow-free roads where deaths occur; for example, many dead on A9 at Drumochter-Dalwhinnie 30th April 1967. Song from 7th February. Departs in August, numbers remain until late September–October, stragglers in November–January.

Shorelark *Eremophila alpestris*
(Irregular rare breeder)

A male singing in mountains on 20th–23rd June 1973, was followed by another same area on 18th May 1976. In 1977, three males and a female were seen and on 25th June a pair with a nest containing three eggs was found. The first and only breeding record for Britain. Flying young were later seen on 12th August and 7th September. In the same year a male was seen on another mountain on 23rd June 1977 but none have been seen since.

Sand Martin *Riparia riparia*
(Numerous summer visitor and breeder)

Breeds throughout the district; mainly in river banks, exposed banks beside roads and in sand quarries; has nested to 500 metres a.s.l. at Drumochter. Largest colonies on River Spey; about 200 holes Pityoulish 1st May 1961 and 290 holes, 130 in use, on 24th July 1987; 150 holes Speybank 5th May 1961 and 126 used holes there in 1994. Other colonies of 77 holes at Ballintean and 85 holes Kingussie in 1994. A decline took place in late 1960s and early 1970s, as in most of western Europe, but the population is now high again. Colonies move in when new sand banks exposed.

Spring arrival: first birds usually 14–27th April but earlier records in five years between 29th March and 7th April, earliest one Loch Insh 25th March 1977. Spring build-up in May, 300 Loch Insh 2nd May and 600 on 12th May 1989, 300 Loch Garten 20th April 1989. High numbers congregate over lochs and marshes in July and August Peak counts: 1,000 Loch Garten 19th August 1994; 500 Loch Insh 19th July 1979 and 700 on 31st July 1989. Departs August, late records in September, last record 20 Loch Garten 29th September 1986. Birds ringed at Kincraig have been recovered in Essex and France; birds in Yorkshire and Sussex (two) have been recovered at Kincraig and Newtonmore.

Swallow *Hirundo rustica*
(Common summer visitor and breeder)

Swallows nest throughout the district at farms, crofts and isolated buildings. Population low in some years, for example, 1962, 1979 and 1994. Spring arrivals usually 17–26th April, but earlier in 1971, 1979 and 1981, with very early single birds at Slochd 25th March 1989 and Loch Garten 31st March 1989. Sometimes, first ones do not arrive until May when numbers build up. Nesting season extends from May to late August; brood still in nest Tulloch 27th August 1973.

Has occurred in high mountains in summer; for example, single birds Cairngorms June 1964 and 24th June 1977 at 1,200 metres a.s.l.. Flocks congregate prior to emigration, 500 at Loch Insh 8th August 1974, 26th August 1975 and 22nd July 1976; 300 Loch Mallachie 31st August 1977.

Most depart late August–early September, with reasonable scatter of sightings into October, for example, 16 Loch Garten 11th October and four on 14th October 1980; latest records five Insh 25th October 1973 and one 31st October 1987.

House Martin *Delichon urbica*
(Numerous summer visitor and breeder)

Nests on dwellings throughout the area, including houses in glens and rarely under bridges. Population low in 1962 and 1980 and in recent years. Nesting season May–August. Spring arrivals usually from mid-May, earliest records one Insh Marshes 4th April; three Loch Garten 20th April 1977, single birds Insh 22nd April 1976 and Loch Garten 29th April 1979. Summer flocks of 100 Insh 26th August 1974, 75 on 2nd September 1978 and 200 in August 1986. Most depart August–early September, 70 flew S over Loch Garten 25th August 1973; late ones to 28th September with four Loch Garten 14th October 1980.

Tree Pipit *Anthus trivialis*
(Common summer visitor and breeder)

Nests throughout district in forest clearings and edges of coniferous, mixed and deciduous woods, also in open woodland. Quite plentiful in some areas but numbers vary. Common Bird Census (CBC) work at Loch Garten showed changes from five to nine pairs in consecutive years; 12–15 pairs nest on Insh reserve. First spring arrivals usually between 23–28th April, early records 16th, 17th and 20th, earliest 12th April 1981. Flocks occur, for example, 50 Tulloch 20th April 1980; also congregates, after breeding, with tit flocks. Departs August, small numbers in September, last record Insh 3rd October 1974.

Meadow Pipit *Anthus pratensis*
(Common summer visitor and breeder, scarce in winter)

Widespread breeder from low-ground moors, marshes and forest bogs right up to the highest plateaux; commonest on moors and grasslands below 800 metres a.s.l.; 60–80 pairs Insh Marshes 1976. Spring arrivals late March with main arrivals in early April; egg-laying late April, late May in mountains. Flocks congregate in July, and also occur on high ground; passage August–October. Peak counts: 176 Insh 5th August 1977, late peak 108 Insh 8th November 1980. Very small numbers occur December–February, high count of 18 Glen Banchor 13th December 1987.

Yellow Wagtail *Motacilla flava*
(Vagrant)

Five records since first in 1966, all in spring–summer:
Male Aviemore 5th August 1966.
Female Alvie 16th May 1981.
One Insh Marshes 27th May 1982.
One Avielochan 29th May 1991.
One Grantown-on-Spey 1st July 1991.

Grey Wagtail *Motacilla cinerea*
(Numerous summer visitor and breeder, rare in winter)

Nests near lochs, rivers and burns throughout area from Advie to Loch Laggan, also into high glens. Not as common at Pied Wagtail; for example, five pairs nesting on Spey between Kincraig and Boat of Garten May 1961; population very low after 1961–2 severe winter and very rare in 1963 after another severe winter. Numbers slow to recover. Generally arrives in late March, early return five Insh 8th March 1975. Maximum counts after nesting, 20 Insh 19th June 1975, 18 on 18th August 1981; 16 Newtonmore sewage works 6th August 1993. Departs September; stragglers in October, rare in November–February, occasionally at

Kingussie sewage works. One Cairn Lochan summit 21st May 1981 and 3rd June 1990.

Pied Wagtail *Motacilla alba*
(Common migrant breeder, rare in winter)

Nests throughout the district around farms and habitations, by lochs, along rivers and roads. At least 10 pairs by river Spey between Kincraig and Aviemore May 1961. Spring arrivals usually from early March, first dates confused by small numbers of overwintering birds. Numbers quick to build up, 60+ Insh 12th April 1975, 18 Loch Garten roost 30th March 1980. Communal roosts occur in late summer; 65 Insh 18th August 1981; 63 Kingussie High School 23rd August 1992; emigration in August–September, stragglers to November and very scarce December to February.

An Aviemore ringed juvenile recovered Bedford in February while birds ringed at Dingwall in September and Hampshire in December have been found in the valley.

White Wagtails, *M.a.alba*, occur as scarce migrants, principally en route to or from Iceland, between 24th March to 22nd May and 13th July to 23rd September, mainly on low ground but also recorded on mountain plateaux in July. Maximum count seven Kingussie 4th September 1972; five arrived Tulloch and four at Avielochan on 23rd September 1989. Pair nest building Abernethy 14th April 1971; mixed pairs recorded breeding three to four times; for example Insh in 1977 and 1978.

Waxwing *Bombycilla garrulus*
(Irregular scarce to numerous winter visitor

Common in irruption years but in other years often rare;

sometimes there is an interesting spring passage. Good years 1958–9, 1963–4, 1965–6, 1967–8, 1974–5, 1975–6, 1986–7 and 1991–2. Autumn arrivals usually in November and December, although from 12th October in 1988. Maximum counts 100+ Nethy Bridge 7th November 1963, 100+ Rothiemurchus 16–17th November 1965, 121 Tulloch 30th December 1974, 52 Aviemore 23rd November 1990. Numbers are usually lower in January. 50 Insh January 1989, but a build up in some years in February–April. Very common, at least 300, possibly 1,000, between Kingussie and Nethy Bridge in January 1968.

Spring flocks often take up residence in areas of juniper bushes on moorland where they feed on juniper and cowberries and sometimes display before emigrating to Scandinavia. Peaks include 55 Tulloch 22nd February 1964, 42 on 24th April 1971, 30 Loch an Eilein 25th April 1973, 56 Tulloch on 25th April 1975. Latest records, 14 Glenmore 7th May 1976, 15 Nethy Bridge 7th May 1989, two Tulloch 18th May 1975, one Loch

Garten 31st May 1968; also one record Abernethy Forest 30th June 1975.

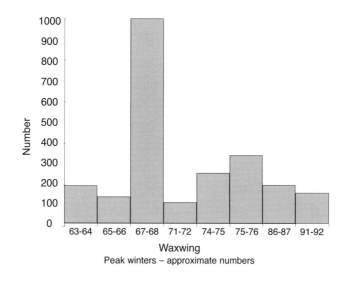

Waxwing
Peak winters – approximate numbers

Dipper *Cinclus cinclus*
(Numerous resident breeder)

Well distributed on rivers and burns from Advie to the highest headwaters, occasionally visits highest burns at 1,300 metres a.s.l. on both sides Lairig Ghru. Population high in good years; six pairs on Spey between Aviemore and Boat of Garten 1st May 1961; four pairs on Leth Allt Beag and Mor, Cromdale 12th June 1989; four pairs Insh Marshes 1994. Affected by severe winters, for example, only one pair Coire Garblach river after severe winter of 1961–2 compared to four to five pairs in 1961.

Birds often sing in winter; egg-laying from mid-March; fledged young on 26th April: second clutches in May. High altitude birds move down to river Spey and to lochs in winter especially in severe cold; single birds at Loch Garten 17th March 1986 and 16th–27th November 1988. Counts: seven

Newtonmore 28th December 1993 and five Broomhill 4th December 1987. A bird showing characteristics of the black-bellied race from Scandinavia at Loch an Eilein 14th October 1978.

Wren *Troglodytes troglodytes*
(Common resident breeder)

Widespread and common throughout the whole district, breeding in marshes, woodland, farmlands and gardens, also in broken moorland and cliffs, even to high level cliffs in the mountains, where they remain even in winter. Numbers much affected by severe winters, high population in mid 1970s crashed after severe weather in January–February 1978, following which only 12 pairs in Loch Garten study area compared to 70 pairs in 1977. 40 pairs Insh Marshes in 1975 but drastic reduction after February 1978. Population often slow to recover, another major crash after 1981–2 winter when none in Loch Garten study area after 32 pairs in 1981. Reasonable numbers at present time.

Dunnock *Prunella modularis*
(Numerous resident breeder)

Breeds in small numbers throughout district, mainly agricultural, lowland areas and near habitations, also in forest clearings and mixed woodland. Sings from early February, earliest 19th January. three to five pairs usually breed Insh but after severe weather in 1981–2 was absent for a year. Probably some local movements as most live near houses and farms in winter. One Cairngorm summit 1st April 1990.

Robin *Erithacus rubecula*
(Common resident breeder and migrant)

112

Nests throughout district in forests with scrub underneath, agricultural and marshy ground and around villages. The true forest birds in Abernethy and Rothiemurchus to 400 metres a.s.l. are summer visitors March to August, but small numbers winter around villages and farms and in marshy low ground. Numbers fluctuate depending on severity of winters, for example 40–50 pairs Loch Garten woods dropped to 20–30 pairs after severe winter of 1978–9. One found dead on snow field on Braeriach at 1,300 metres a.s.l. in June 1941. One ringed Whalsay, Shetland 3rd April 1978 (overshooting spring migrant) was recorded at Aviemore 20 days later; while an August juvenile moved from Carrbridge to Dundee in six weeks.

Bluethroat *Luscinia svecica*
(Vagrant migrant and breeder)

The first recorded nesting attempt in the United Kingdom occurred at the Insh Marshes in 1968 when a female was flushed from a nest containing three eggs on 13th June. There were six eggs on 20th, which failed to hatch; no male was observed so the female may not have mated. One male singing near Cat Lodge 15th June 1980, not present next day. In 1985 a pair reared five young in the Insh Marshes and this was the first successful breeding for the United Kingdom. A male seen in Boat of Garten 23rd May 1987 and the remains of one killed by a predator on Cairn Lochan on the same day.

Black Redstart *Phoenicurus ochruros*
(Vagrant)

Five records since the first one in 1947:
One first year male Glen Tromie 5th November 1947.

One Ryvoan Pass 18th December 1987.
One Cairngorm 18th July 1989.
Female Coire an Lochain cliffs 3rd August 1990.
Male singing Braes of Castle Grant 18th May 1992.

Redstart *Phoenicurus phoenicurus*
(Common summer visitor and breeder)

Nests throughout woods and forests, well distributed in mature open Scots pine forests as well as in birch and mixed woods. Very plentiful Rothiemurchus 1952 and Abernethy/Rothiemurchus 1960–63. Scarcer some summers, for example 1969, and numbers also low 1970–3 and 1975. 20–25 pairs Loch Garten 1979 but only 15 pairs in 1981. Spring arrival usually late April, earliest dates 10th April 1988, 11th April 1981 and 16th April 1980 all at Loch Garten, usually few days later in Badenoch. Egg-laying late May; breeding success generally good in nest boxes. Gathers with mixed tit flocks in July; also one Geal Charn at 900 metres a.s.l., July 1979. Departs August–early September; late date one Inshriach 7th October 1969.

Whinchat *Saxicola rubetra*
(Numerous summer visitor and breeder)

Nests throughout glens, mainly forest edges and larger clearings, moorland scrub and marshy areas, especially where there is bog myrtle. Scarce some summers and in recent decade. For example eight pairs Insh Marshes in 1985, now two to three pairs. Spring arrivals mainly from second week May, earliest Insh Marshes 21st April; Loch Gamnha 27th April and Loch Garten 28th April 1977. Nesting season extended with second broods in August. One migrant Braeriach at 1,000 metres a.s.l. 22nd July 1979.

Departs July to mid-September, latest records Insh Marshes 6th October 1981 and 27th October 1975.

Stonechat *Saxicola torquata*
(Irregular scarce breeder and local migrant)

Irregularly breeds in small numbers in the district but much affected by severe winters. Reasonable population in Abernethy 1890s; scarce Rothiemurchus 1947–8, bred Glenmore 1950–4 with four broods in 1952. One pair bred successfully Glenmore 1961 but none in 1962. After two severe winters was very scarce in the next decade with definitely no reports of breeding 1968–72. Increase in 1973 with records at six sites, maximum three Tulloch 26th November; further increase 1974 when at least six nesting pairs known (three in Glenmore); high numbers also in 1975, lower in 1976 but increase in 1977 and 1978 with about six nesting pairs reported; only one pair known in 1979. None recorded on migration or nesting 1980 and 1981 after severe winters. None until 1988–9, when one pair reared three broods near Dalwhinnie in 1989. At least eight pairs located in 1990, some with double broods, while in 1993 there were four pairs in Glen Tromie.

Wheatear *Oenanthe oenanthe*
(Numerous summer visitor and breeder)

Widespread on open moors, at all levels from valley floor to mountain tops (1,300 metres a.s.l.), scarcer at higher altitudes, more plentiful in western grassier areas, especially where there are stony outcrops. Increased afforestation has lowered numbers overall. Spring arrivals mainly early April; first records Inshriach 25th March 1972 and pair Tulloch 26th March 1973, arrived on

29th March in five years in last 30. Young birds in July and August often feed on highest plateaux. Most depart in August, becoming scarce after mid-September. Greenland migrants identified 4th October 1971 and 10th October 1973. Last record Spey Dam 31st October 1972.

Ring Ouzel *Turdus torquatus*
(Numerous summer visitor and breeder)

Patchy distribution in upper parts of glens and burns, cliffs and rocky moorland, mainly between 500 and 800 metres a.s.l.. Fewer in higher mountains where they may breed to 1,300 metres a.s.l. in Cairngorms. Numbers can be high in some areas; abundant upper Strathnethy and 10 pairs Glen Einich 1950s, six to ten pairs Mam Suim 29th May 1963 and about 20 pairs Gaick 25th April 1961. Spring arrivals from March, earliest records Killiehuntly 25th March 1990, two Slochd 28th March 1972.

First young fly in late May; gathers in flocks to eat mountain berries in August; for example 20 Cairn Lochan 20th August 1989. Most depart September; latest record Strathnethy 13th November 1983. A 1953 chick ringed in Glen Feshie was recovered in the French Pyrenees on 1st April 1954. Some Scandinavian migrants pass through with thrush flocks in late autumn; for example five Insh Marshes 5th November 1994 and seven on 6th November, at the same time as records of this species on Moray Firth coast. Otherwise rare migrant at Insh Marshes with only five single birds 1973–93.

Blackbird *Turdus merula*
(Common resident breeder and migrant)

Widespread around villages, houses and farmland, also at lower densities in mixed woodland and forests. Resident near habitations but true forest breeders take up territories in March and depart in August. Small numbers occur on migration in March; sometimes good numbers pass through with Fieldfares and Redwings in October–November; maximum counts 200 Rothiemurchus 20th October 1971 and 60 Insh 5th November 1976. One Braeriach summit (1,300 metres a.s.l.) 19th July 1925.

Fieldfare *Turdus pilaris*
(Rare irregular breeder; common migrant)

In 1970 a pair nested and fledged six young 16–17th June; adult found freshly dead near the 1970 site in 1973 and a pair in suitable nesting area 2nd July 1976. Pair alarm calling, probably with nest, Laggan June 1986; bred Newtonmore in 1980s and one pair bred Insh Marshes and reared three young in 1993. Pair near Laggan 20th June 1989. Autumn migration mainly in October and November; small numbers in September, maximum 100 Insh 24th September 1967, early date 4th. Annual numbers vary and length of stay in district depends on rowan berry crop; many flocks arrive in area at great height after crossing North Sea and make first landfall inland rather than on coast The birds strip rowan trees on passage and generally move south. Peak counts 3,000–4,000 Nethy Bridge 3rd November 1963, 1,000 Insh 14th November 1976, 2,000 Insh 20–23rd October 1982, 5,000 Insh Marshes November 1989 and 12,000 on 28th October 1992. Also occurs on mountains during this migration; Winter numbers usually low; maximum 44 Insh 21st January 1979. Main spring passage March–April, has been later in 1970s with flocks even in early May. 100 Kinchurdy 17th April 1973; 100 Insh 10th April 1977, late peak 50 Insh 6th May 1974.

Song Thrush *Turdus philomelus*
(Numerous or common breeder, rare in winter)

Thinly spread throughout district, mainly agricultural areas, mixed woodland and near habitation. Fourteen to sixteen pairs breed Insh Marshes and breeding numbers appear to be holding up, although possibly some recent decrease. Returns in late February, usually 23rd–26th; early dates three singing Tulloch 15th February 1980 and 18th February 1981. Usually returns in numbers on first dates and immediate song.

Egg-laying from mid-April with flying young by 3rd May. Small flocks feed on bird cherries in August–early September and then depart. Some passage in October, and in mild winters a few winter in the valley.

Redwing *Turdus iliacus*
(Rare breeder; common passage migrant, scarce in winter)

This species colonised the district in the late 1960s; there were singing birds in 1943 (two), 1947 and 1948 but it was not until 1968 that two pairs nested and single males sang at two other sites. Since then has been recorded nesting and/or singing every summer: with peaks of three pairs and seven males in 1971; five pairs and 12 males in 1982 and five pairs and six males in 1990. Breeding birds are of continental origin.

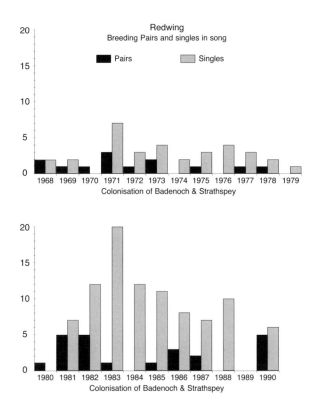

Redwing
Breeding Pairs and singles in song

Colonisation of Badenoch & Strathspey

Colonisation of Badenoch & Strathspey

Autumn passage from mid-September, mainly October with very large flocks passing through some years. Peak days: thousands in valley on 15–17th October 1971; at Insh 1,500 10th October 1972, 1,000 on 20–24th October 1977 and 15–17th October 1980, 1,500+ on 20th October 1982, 8,000+

in October 1986, 2,000 Tulloch and 2,500 Insh Marshes October 1992. Numbers low in November; scarce December–February; return passage is small, maximum 80 Doune 9th March 1961 and 55 Rothiemurchus 28th March 1973. Sometimes occurs on high mountain plateaux on autumn passage.

Mistle Thrush *Turdus viscivorus*
(Common breeder, most depart for winter)

Breeds throughout district mainly in woods surrounding agricultural land and near villages and large gardens. Arrival on territories from mid-February, earlier in recent years; song on arrival, first heard 15th February 1981. Small flocks in spring in snowy weather, 10 Guislich 4th March 1972; egg-laying from first week April.

After the young fledge, birds gather together in flocks in July and August to forage on moorland berries; often mistaken for Fieldfares by visitors when in distant flocks. Maximum 115 Tulloch 21st August 1988 and 100 Insh 23rd August 1986. Many depart in August and September but some remain and are joined by migrants, with other thrushes, in October; peak counts at Insh Marshes 100 on 21st September 1981 and 150 on 13th October 1980.

Occasional small flocks in winter, 11 Alvie 1st January 1973; pairs sometimes visit territories in fine weather in December–January.

Grasshopper Warbler *Locustella naevia*
(Scarce summer visitor and breeder)

Recorded annually at Insh Marshes 4th May to 18th August, earliest 23rd April 1987, latest 13th September. Between two and nine birds heard singing in summer, best years 1971, 1973 and 1975 with breeding proved in 1974. Has increased in recent years with peaks of 25 singing males in 1986, 15 in 1992 and 21 in 1993. One Tulloch 1977, where probably nested in 1979; also present 1980 and 1994. One singing Glenmore 6–13th May 1983 and 28th May 1984.

Sedge Warbler *Acrocephalus schoenobaenus*
(Numerous summer visitor and breeder)

Good numbers nest in marshy areas beside lochs and rivers throughout the district. Best area is Insh Marshes where estimates of 55–80 pairs in the 1970s and a census count of 145 males singing in 1992. Twelve singing birds Kinrara bog 10th May 1961. Spring arrivals in early May, usually second week, earliest Insh Marshes 3rd May 1981 but earlier in recent decade, 24th April 1987 and 25th April 1988. Departs August, last usually in early September, late one Insh Marshes 29th September 1972.

Marsh Warbler *Acrocephalus palustris*
(Vagrant)

Male singing at Laggan 9th June 1988; another species which may start to breed in Scotland.

Great Reed Warbler *Acrocephalus arundinaceus*
(Vagrant)

Male in song in at Ruthven, Insh Marshes 8–20th June 1964.

Icterine Warbler *Hippolais icterina*
(Vagrant breeder)

A pair found breeding in deciduous bushes at Creag Meagaidh National Nature Reserve in July 1992; they were feeding young when found. This is the first breeding record for Scotland; in 1992 there was an unprecedented fall of about 150 spring migrants in Scotland, mainly in Orkney and Shetland.

Lesser Whitethroat *Sylvia curruca*
(Rare visitor)

Used to be a vagrant but since the 1980s has increased and may breed in the future. Single birds singing Glenmore 6th July 1941 and 14th June 1951, and Carrbridge 25th May 1977. In 1981 an unusual influx, male singing Tulloch 18–21st June and at Pityoulish, one on 14th June two on 16th and three (two in song) on 23rd June. Male singing Nethy Bridge 26th June 1986.

Since 1987 singing birds have been noted between 17th May and 30th June from Nethy Bridge to Newtonmore. The yearly totals of individuals are 1987 (three), 1988 (three), 1989 (one), 1991 (one), 1992 (two), 1993(one) and 1994 (one).

Whitethroat *Sylvia communis*
(Scarce summer visitor and local breeder)

Small numbers nest in drier areas of broom/gorse or raspberry/blackthorn in agricultural areas up to 350 metres a.s.l., but mainly along river valley between Advie and Kingussie. Numbers are low and there were more before 1970. At Kincraig, a regular nesting area, there were none between 1978 and 1982 but numbers have recovered to four pairs, after first pair bred again in 1984. Spring arrivals in mid-May, earliest dates Insh Marshes 24th April 1987, two Tulloch 9th May 1962, one Insh 11th May 1973; departs August, last record Tulloch 17th August 1971.

Garden Warbler *Syliva borin*
(Scarce summer visitor and local breeder)

Single birds recorded in song in 1952, 1955 and 1961 after first record Aviemore 4th June 1951. Since 1968, when nesting was confirmed at Grantown-on-Spey and Newtonmore, the species has increased in mixed deciduous woodland near agricultural land and villages, especially in areas of bird cherry along the main rivers.

First recorded breeding as far west as Kinlochlaggan in 1978 and recorded in eight to ten areas in 1981. Spring arrivals in late May, earliest 11th May 1990 at Insh Marshes where peak of six singing birds in 1986. One on passage on Carn Ban Mor at 1,000 metres a.s.l., on 27th May 1978. Gathers in late summer to feed on bird cherries, departs August–September, last record Rothiemurchus 7th September 1969.

Blackcap *Sylvia atricapilla*
(Scarce summer visitor, migrant and winter visitor)

This species has not been proved breeding in the district although one was seen nest building at Rothiemurchus on 13th June 1976. Singing birds have been recorded at the Doune Garden, Rothiemurchus in 1952, 1961 and in seven years between 1968 and 1981; there were two males in 1976. Singing males were recorded at 10 sites in the 1980s, including two at Pattack 28th May 1981. Old record from Forest Lodge 1895.

One or two nearly annually between 9th October and 11th March from 1954–94; including two Newtonmore 12th October 1972, two Kingussie 28–29th November 1983, three Kingussie January 1987, one long stay Grantown-on-Spey 10th February to 11th March 1988 and two Kingussie December 1994.

Wood Warbler *Phylloscopus sibilatrix*
(Numerous summer visitor and breeder)

Small numbers breed in beech, oak and mature birch woods in
the district, especially Rothiemurchus, Inshriach and Alvie.
Recorded Aviemore district 1894, noticeably more there in 1895;
these annual variations occur to this day, for example 18 males
noted between Kingussie and Nethy Bridge in 1965 but only
three in same areas in 1968. Twelve males Inshriach to Inverdruie
in 1952; eight males in song Insh Marshes in best year, normally
four to five pairs. Good numbers in 1981, especially Speybank to
Kinrara. Spring arrivals in mid-May earliest Rothiemurchus 5th
May 1895; egg-laying early June; departs in August.

Chiffchaff *Phylloscopus collybitta*
(Rare irregular breeder, scarce visitor)

One pair proved nesting at Carrbridge, feeding young on 14th
June 1972. Singing birds, usually one or two per year every year
since 1960 except 1963–5, 1973 and 1978 and apparently less
frequently in recent years. Best years 1979, 1981 and 1987 when
singing birds in five areas. Has been recorded at Insh Marshes in
12 out of 28 springs. Recorded between 6th April and 1st July;
monthly totals to 1984 April (12), May (nine), June (six) and
July (two), three autumn Single birds between 1–28th September.
Two winter records: single birds at Newtonmore 23rd December
1984 and 9th January 1989.

Willow Warbler *Phylloscopus trochilus*
(Common summer visitor and breeder)

Widespread breeding species throughout the whole district in birch woods, forest edges, clearings and marshy land, even right up glens to the last straggling birches. Twenty pairs in 564 acres at Insh Marshes in 1977 and 100 pairs on whole reserve in 1990s. Comparative census counts at Loch Garten show fluctuations from 80 pairs in 1979, to 73 pairs in 1980 but only 53 pairs in 1981 after late cold spring.

Spring arrivals from second half April (14–25th), earliest Insh 11th April 1981, Loch Garten 12th April 1975; build up usually rapid after first singing arrivals. Egg-laying from early May; gathers in flocks with tits in July, maximum day count 175 Insh Marshes 7th August 1977; moves out in August, one Einich Carn 900 metres a.s.l., on 2nd August 1981. Stragglers in September to 20th, late records Garten 2nd October 1978 and Insh Marshes 3rd October. An amazingly rapid ringing recovery from Isle of May of a Willow Warbler ringed on 5th May 1956 found Grantown-on-Spey on 6th May. On 8th June 1986 a bird singing at Loch Vaa was considered to be a hybrid between this species and a Greenish Warbler *Phylloscopus trochiloides*.

Goldcrest *Regulus regulus*
(Common resident breeder)

Nests throughout the district in coniferous forests, mixed woodlands and large exotic conifers. Population crashes after very cold winters; numbers in 1962 down to one–tenth after a severe winter, the worst affected species; recovers quite quickly with egg-laying from late April and some double-broods.

Censuses at Loch Garten study plots gave 72 pairs in 1977 followed by decreases to 42 pairs in 1978 and 15 pairs in 1979 after cold winter, then increased to 21 pairs and 25 pairs in 1980 and 1981. Big decrease noted at Insh in 1982. Song recorded from 10th February. Joins tit flocks in late summer to winter and may be seen anywhere in glens, even one found dead Cairngorm summit 17th July 1976.

Spotted Flycatcher *Muscicapa striata*
(Numerous summer visitor and breeder)

Nests throughout the district in mature open coniferous forests, mixed and deciduous woods, large gardens in villages and farms; widespread but not plentiful. Spring arrivals from mid-May, first dates usually 12–16th May, earliest records Newtonmore 8th May 1962 and Kingussie 9th May 1977. Numbers fluctuate: Loch Garten 11 pairs in 1979 but only five pairs in same area in 1980. Gathers in mixed species flocks and starts to depart late July–August, maximum count 35 Insh Marshes 5th August 1977; last records in early September; latest Loch Garten 14th September 1981, two Newtonmore 19th September 1983, one Insh Marshes 24th September.

Pied Flycatcher *Ficedula hypoleuca*
(Scarce summer visitor and breeder)

Recorded summer 1868; two pairs bred Aviemore area 1948 and 1960–1, one pair in 1962. Up to 10 males recorded in 1969; known to breed in 1971, 1973, 1977 (two pairs), 1978 and 1979–83 (three to ten pairs each year). Principally in mature deciduous woods and pine forests and in riverside woodland from Kingussie to Nethy Bridge.

Since then has become regular, especially in nest boxes between Aviemore and Insh. Best years 1984 (18 nests), 1986 (14) and 1990 (16); breeding success often excellent, for example, 13 nests with total of 60 young in 1990, but failures in other years because of bad weather and red squirrel predation. Spring arrivals from 1st May, mainly mid-May; emigration July to August, latest 17th August.

Long-tailed Tit *Aegithalos caudatus*
(Common resident breeder)

Nests throughout the district from Advie to Loch Laggan, mainly in lower and wetter, mixed and deciduous woodland and shrub areas, common in birch woods. Population low after severe winters of 1961–2 and 1962–3; numbers high in 1971–2 after succession of mild winters. Maximum counts 48 Insh Marshes 23rd August 1972 and 40+ Loch Garten 31st August 1980 and 36 there on 19th October 1987. Sometimes visits bird tables in winter. One ringed Aviemore 10th December 1964 still living Aviemore 19th October 1968.

Willow Tit *Parus montanus*
(Used to be scarce resident breeder but now extinct in district)

In 1891, plentiful in birch woods at Kingussie, just north of Kincraig, Kinrara and near Boat of Garten (seven to ten in a flock). Several Loch an Eilein 15th May 1889, two nests found Aviemore 1893 and numerous Kincraig 25th September 1895. Young recorded at Balavil 1914; well distributed in 1919 when one seen at 700 metres a.s.l., in Cairngorms on 7th September. Present at Dulnain Bridge, Dorback, Boat of Garten, Rothiemurchus and Kingussie 1937–41 but scarce in 1948. Probably crashed in severe winters of late 1940s and early 1950s when species became extinct. No acceptable records in the last three decades.

Crested Tit *Parus cristatus*
(Numerous resident breeder)

One of the special birds of the old Caledonian Forest of Strathspey; occurs throughout the pine woods of the district from Advie to Ardverikie, but principally in the Strathspey forests. Commonest in mature old forests but also occurs in rather open deer forest and old conifer plantations. The first two specimens were shot at Carrbridge and described in 1842. In 1890 they were known in the Abernethy, Rothiemurchus, Glenmore and Dulnain forests, being most abundant in Upper Strathspey. Has increased during this century and now well distributed in suitable habitat; population subject to crashes after severe winters like 1947, 1951 and 1981 but not as badly as other tits, probably due to their ability to find food at ground level in long heather. Studies at Loch Garten have shown variations in nesting pairs from a peak of 29 pairs in 1978 to 18 pairs in same area in 1981; in the best areas average density is 0.15 pairs per hectare. Has increased in recent years near Insh Marshes as local pinewoods have matured, and a pair bred for first time on the reserve in 1985. Nests in late

April–May; gathers into mixed flocks in late June and stays in them through rest of year. Small flocks often seen in winter on open moorland and hillsides dotted with old pines where they feed in the heather. Locally, visits bird tables.

Coal Tit *Parus ater*
(Common resident breeder)

The commonest tit in the district; nests throughout all coniferous forests, also occurs in birch woods, mixed woodland and large gardens. Severe drop in numbers after winters of 1947 and 1961–2, when numbers down to less than 20% of 1961 population, but in late 1980s at Loch Garten study area only varied from 42 pairs to 27 pairs. Flocks occur July to March, up to 50 birds recorded in one flock, when they also forage in small woods and scrubland, and visit bird tables.

Blue Tit *Parus caeruleus*
(Common resident breeder)

Commoner and more widespread than Great Tit; occurs in mixed and deciduous woods, including wetter areas and near farms and houses, in fact wherever enough trees or shrubs provide suitable habitat; does not like pure conifer forests, commoner on lower ground. Gathers into mixed flocks outside breeding season, maximum count 103 Insh Marshes September 1988 where 40–5 pairs breed. Visits bird tables.

Great Tit *Parus major*
(Common resident breeder)

Like Blue Tit prefers deciduous woods and scrubland, and near farms and houses, but occurs in any woodland. Often to be seen in autumn and winter near beech trees; frequent visitor to bird tables. Not so affected by weather as other tits; CBC change at Loch Garten from five pairs in 1985 to eight pairs in 1986. Flocks with other species, up to 20. Count on Insh Marshes of 43 in September 1988.

Treecreeper *Certhia familiaris*
(Common resident breeder)

Nests throughout district in all woodlands, even high up glens. 30–40 pairs estimated in best year Loch Garten reserve and less than half this, after run of bad years. Starts to sing from mid-February; joins in mixed tit flocks outside nesting season. As in other parts of United Kingdom, excavates roosting and nesting holes in introduced redwood trees.

Golden Oriole *Oriolus oriolus*
(Vagrant)

Six records of single males:
Male singing Insh 28th May 1977.
Male Aviemore 18th June 1981.
Male Dunachton 11th May 1982, (possibly same as next record).
Male singing Insh Marshes 13th May, 28th May and 1st June 1982.
One flying Scootmore towards Advie 15th June 1991.
Male singing Abernethy Forest 17th May 1992

Red-backed Shrike *Lanius collurio*
(Has bred once; rare visitor)

Single birds Coylumbridge 9th June–July 1947 and 1st June

1954, and Loch Morlich 31st May 1973. In 1977 a pair were located in Abernethy Forest feeding at least two just fledged young on 1st August; also another pair near Carrbridge 6th–10th June. Between 1977 and 1982 was observed in very small numbers (one to three) annually, principally in late May to July, earliest 30th May, mainly male birds. Late migrant eating a House Martin at Etteridge 23rd September 1981, when migrants seen on coast. Since then has become rarer with single males in 1985, 1987, 1988, 1989 and 1992 (two) between 28th May and 9th August; no suggestion of breeding although single males have spent extended stays at one site in Badenoch from 28th May to 9th August 1985 and 8th–23rd July 1989. One autumn migrant Abernethy in September 1993.

Great Grey Shrike *Lanius excubitor*
(Rare to scarce migrant and winter visitor)

Single birds Spey Bridge, Grantown-on-Spey December 1909, Drumguish 1st May 1947, 29th December 1952 and 15–20th March 1953, Kingussie 2nd November 1952 and Achlean 27th February 1953. Seen every year from 1960–83 except winters of

1964–5, 1968–9, 1969–70 and 1975–6; 70 individuals recorded in the remaining winters, best totals 10 in 1970–1 and eight in 1966–7. First autumn record 13th October and latest 6th May; monthly totals of individuals present in each month are October (nine), November (18), December (19), January (14), February (16), March (14), April (18) and May (five). Some used to stay over winter, usually in wetter areas with scattered bushes and trees, such as Insh Marshes or on larger mosses in forests; longest recorded stay October to 18th March. Spring migrants sometimes took up territories for two to three weeks with occasional song.

Since 1984 has been much rarer with winter records only in 1984 (three), 1986 (two), 1987 (three), 1988 (two), 1990 (one), 1992 (one) and 1994 (one). Sightings between 12th November to 23th April, with no long stays or over wintering.

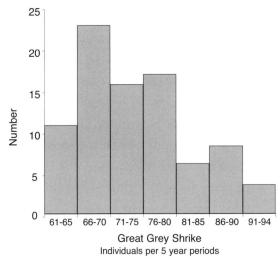

Great Grey Shrike
Individuals per 5 year periods

Jay *Garrulus glandarius*
(Vagrant)

Two old records and four since 1985:
One shot Grantown-on-Spey about 1890–4.
One found dead killed by Peregrine, Gaick mid 1960s.
One Pityoulish 16th September 1985.
One Dell of Killiehuntly 30th June 1989.
One Tromie Bridge 26th–28th September 1993.
One Dorback October 1993.

Magpie *Pica pica*
(Rare resident breeder)

Nests locally in thickets and plantations in agricultural land; haunts livestock feeders in winters. Plentiful around Grantown-on-Spey in 1890s; a Strathspey census in 1938 reported four pairs within one mile of Dulnain Bridge, three pairs between there and Boat of Garten, six pairs within two miles of Nethy Bridge, three other pairs in Abernethy and Glenmore and birds seen in Aviemore and Kincraig. In 1960–2 there were breeding pairs at Cluny Castle, Insh Marshes, Inverdruie, West and East Croftmore (Pityoulish), Wester Tulloch, Tulloch, Nethy Bridge and Broomhill; there were probably more as no systematic search was made. By 1968 only six pairs were known between Kingussie and Nethy Bridge; the decrease continued and the only known pairs in 1971–3 were at East and West Croftmore and Broomhill. In the late 1970s, the Pityoulish birds were the only regular nesting records, with stragglers to Tulloch and one Nethy Bridge 12th June 1981. An increase from the early 1980s, for example, pair nested Insh Marshes 1983, and by late 1980s was breeding in Tulloch, Pityoulish, Boat-of-Garten, Aviemore and Carrbridge. Possibly as high as 15 pairs in district but use of Larsen traps has reduced population again. An albino occurred at Pityoulish 9th March 1971.

Jackdaw *Corvus monedula*
(Common resident and breeder)

Nests throughout district in lower rocky cliffs, such as Creag Dubh (Newtonmore) and Craigellachie, also in larger rookeries and in old buildings (for example, Loch an Eilein Castle) as well as house chimneys. Returns to nest sites in mid-March; egg-laying from mid-April. Recommences communal roosting in late June when congregates at night with rooks; main roosts at Coylumbridge, 2,000 on 26th January 1973, now moved to Aviemore; Laggan, 500 on 22nd January 1972.

Rook *Corvus frugilegus*
(Common resident and breeder)

Nineteen known rookeries in district in 1975 from Cromdale to

Garvamore, in Scots Pine clumps at lower level near farmland. Rookery count in 1975 gave 2020 nests, largest rookery at Dulnain Bridge with 318 nests. Counts from early 1960s suggest little change in numbers and this is confirmed by roost counts. Possibly some recent declines. Nests in March; first young calling in nests Broomhill 13th April 1971.

Newly fledged broods move to upland crofting areas, such as Tulloch, in late June, for example, 47 Tulloch 30th July 1994. Main winter roost in pines at Coylumbridge has moved in recent years to Aviemore where 4,000–5,000 congregate at night; the noisy roosting flights are a feature of winter evenings. Smaller roosts near Cluny Castle and Grantown-on-Spey, and recently at Loch Garten where 120 on 14th September 1994. A straggler seen Wells of Dee, Braeriach 15th July 1925.

Carrion Crow *Corvus corone*
(Common resident and breeder)

Badenoch and Strathspey is an area of overlap between Carrion and Hooded Crows; there is much mixed breeding and hybrids are common; nowadays Carrion Crows are much commoner. Hoodies are more regular in the western hill areas of Badenoch, while dark birds are more plentiful in the valley floor and forested areas. In 1890s Carrion Crows were quite scarce. Crows nest to the highest glens, usually in trees but also cliff and ground nesting in some places.

Communal roosts occur, for example, in Abernethy Forest where 500+ throughout each winter in the early 1960s, less in 1970s (probably effect of moorland poison baits) with only 175 in 1972, 240 in 1981 and 227 on 12th October 1986, now rarer. Roost is used by non-breeders in summer, 90 on 25th July 1972. With advent of Larsen traps population in many areas is now much reduced. Since the 1960s regularly visits Cairngorm plateaux and this is a threat to nesting Dotterel and other mountain nesting birds. A chick Carrion Crow ringed at Paisley 19th July 1967 was recovered at Kingussie 16th May 1968.

Raven *Corvus corax*
(Rare resident breeder, scarce winter visitor)

Only one or two pairs now breed while 30 years ago the species nested in 25 or more sites throughout district, mainly in Upper Strathspey and Badenoch. Numbers high after last war with a large winter roost on Dava Moor; well distributed in early 1960s but since then has suffered severely from illegal poisoning and also from decline in sheep stocks; most traditional sites are now abandoned and nesting records are rare, only two pairs located 1982. Bred at the Slochd in 1990 for the first time in ten years but did not nest again. Wandering birds still occur, especially from Insh westward; some recent increases in winter flocks, 50 near Kingussie 17th December 1983, 36 Tromiebridge on 10th March 1984 and 80 in January 1992 at the regular roost site.

Starling *Sturnus vulgaris*
(Common resident breeder and numerous migrant)

Nests throughout district in villages, farms and isolated buildings, also in natural holes well away from buildings, even in pine forests. Has declined in last two decades. Birds in outlying sites return in March. Gathers into flocks in June–July when first broods feed in newly cut silage and hay fields, most depart late summer. Peak counts: 3,000 Insh Marshes reed beds 10th August 1978, 700 on 27th August 1980 and 500 on 2nd September 1990. Smaller flocks remain in villages throughout winter and used to roost in reed beds in Insh Marshes, Kinrara and Loch Mallachie, also in rhododendrons at Rothiemurchus. One Cairngorm 17th June 1964.

House Sparrow *Passer domesticus*
(Numerous resident breeder)

Now a rather local breeder but used to nest in all towns, villages, farms and some isolated houses. Tree nesting recorded Avielochan 26th May 1961. Used to leave outlying farms during winter and gathered at larger farmyards, especially those with corn stacks. Out door threshing of corn stacks finished in the early 1970s and in recent decades has deserted many farms, crofting townships and smaller villages. Last pair at Tulloch in 1977, one record of a single male for a day since then.

Tree Sparrow *Passer montanus*
(Vagrant)

Rare visitor; may have nested in irruption years. Documented records:
Three Tulloch Moor 11th April 1973.
One Insh 29th May 1977.
One Insh 10th May 1985.
Two Highland Wildlife Park 12th October 1987.

Chaffinch *Fringilla coelebs*
(Common resident breeder and migrant)

Very common breeding bird throughout whole district in pine forests, mixed and deciduous woods, around habitations and farmland; often feeds at lay-bys in summer and can be very tame.

Numbers at Loch Garten study area peaked at 115 pairs in 1980 but down to a low of 77 pairs in 1981. Vacates forests in late summer and spends autumn and winter in flocks on agricultural land, farm yards and gardens.

Returns to woodland territories on fine days in early February, usually only males at start with some song; main arrivals late March–April. Flocks of several hundred regular at most farms in the old days but now scarcer as farm activities have changed. Peak counts 1,000 on flattened corn Pityoulish 9th January 1967, 770 Insh 25th November 1979, 1,000 Tullochgrue 10th March 1982, 1,000 on stubbles Tulloch 27th September 1994. Some part of population might emigrate, several flying over Cairngorm 31st March 1990.

Brambling *Fringilla montifringilla*
(Has bred; scarce autumn and winter visitor)

A pair were seen at Carrbridge with two young on 19th July 1983; there was a pair at the same place 27th May 1982. Single males have been noted in June 1951 (paired with Chaffinch?), June–July 1969, 5th June 1975, 28–29th May 1981, three males in 1982. Also a female at Lochindorb on 25th June 1992 and a hybrid x Chaffinch juvenile was recorded at Newtonmore in July 1971.

Irregular numbers most winters from October to April, some suggestion of spring passage. Usually found in winter near beech trees. Winter peaks: 50 Spey Dam 8–25th November 1969, 50–60 Inverdruie December 1976 and January 1977, 200 Rothiemurchus 15th October 1978, 100 Insh 7th November 1982, 100 Boat of Garten 1st January 1992 and 200 Loch Insh 13th December 1992. Spring build up in 1974 when 700 roosting Loch Garten woods 13th April.

Greenfinch *Carduelis chloris*
(Numerous resident breeder)

Has increased considerably in recent decades as a breeder. Nests throughout district in agricultural and village areas, rare higher up in glens. Gathers in flocks at farm yards, in stubbles and turnip fields in autumn and winter but nowadays very plentiful at nut feeders. Maximum counts 160 Nethy Bridge 10th December 1967, 74 Tulloch 19th February 1979, 80 Insh 4th December 1980 and 124 in September 1988. One ringed near Aberdeen in January found dead at Insh in August.

Goldfinch *Carduelis carduelis*
(Scarce resident breeder)

Very small numbers nest, mainly near gardens and agricultural land, from Grantown-on-Spey to Laggan. Recorded as rare in Badenoch in 1963–5. Apparently commoner since mid-1960s; nesting records from various areas including one pair in 1979 and 1980 in edge of Caledonian forest at Tulloch, and further increase from 1983 with two pairs Loch Laggan in 1986. Flocks include 30 Rothiemurchus November–December 1966 and 50 mid-March 1969, 12 Laggan 22nd January 1972, 20 Insh 22nd January 1976, 64 Insh October 1988 and 60 Kingussie 12th February 1990. One Cairngorm car park 3rd December 1990.

Siskin *Carduelis spinus*
(Common migrant breeder, some winter)

Nests throughout the coniferous forests of the district, mainly in older woods; population highest in old native forests of Abernethy and Rothiemurchus. Nesting numbers very high in 1961 and

1962 at Loch Garten forest, lower in 1960; about 45 pairs Loch Garten reserve in 1978 and 1981 but only about 25–30 pairs in 1979 and 1980. Gathers in flocks in autumn and winter when seen feeding in alders and birches, sometimes with Redpolls. Many depart for southern England in autumn; now regular at nut feeders,especially in late winter–spring. Maximum counts 350 Insh Marshes 1st November 1961, 200 Rothiemurchus 4th January 1988, 200 Glen Banchor 6th December and 450 Kinlochlaggan 8th December 1992. Ten over Cairngorm 26th April 1987.

Linnet *Carduelis cannabina*
(Scarce summer visitor and breeder)

Nests in small numbers on drier agricultural areas, mainly on low ground Aviemore to Advie, few to Laggan. Used to nest at higher crofts but suggestion of decrease in recent decade due to farming changes. Arrives April and early May, departs August and September. Peak counts: 200 Boat of Garten 19th December 1983, 172 Nethy Bridge 3rd March 1991 and 300 Boat of Garten 1st January 1992. Single birds over Cairngorm 29th and 31st March 1990.

Twite *Carduelis flavirostris*
(Scarce resident breeder and migrant)

Widely spread but scarce breeder, has decreased considerably since last century when it was common in crofting townships. Occasional pairs nest on upper crofts and foothills of mountains, Abernethy, Dava Moor and Craigowrie; little commoner in western areas above Laggan and Dalwhinnie.

Rare in higher mountains, for example, three Carn Ban Mor

15th August 1973 and 12 Coire Lochain 27th August 1974. Flocks occur and sometimes over winter in Badenoch, 100 Ruthven marsh 18th September 1973, 200 Insh 29th September 1974 and 100 on 14th March 1977, 100 Creag Meagaidh and Kingussie 21st November 1992.

Smaller flocks in Strathspey, maximum 16 Avielochan 10th October 1973, more in recent years, 58 Nethy Bridge 2nd May and 180 Broomhill 8th December 1991.

Redpoll *Carduelis flammea*
(Numerous migrant breeder)

Widespread breeder in reasonable numbers throughout district in a variety of young deciduous woods and scrub habitats, often in wetter areas. Population noted as high in 1961 and 1962. Gathers in flocks in autumn and winter when often seen in birch woods and marshy areas. Peak counts 300 Insh November–December 1974, 350 in February–March 1977 and 400 on 19th September 1992; 300 Loch an Eilein 29th March 1975; 500 Rothiemurchus 4th January 1988 and 400 Abernethy October 1993. A bird ringed in October 1965 in Cheshire recovered at Balavil in May 1967, while a Lancashire bird ringed on 15th April 1978 was recovered at Insh 6th July 1978. Mealy Redpoll migrants have been recorded: two to three Insh Marshes 25th October 1972 and one 22nd February 1974. A Greenland Redpoll seen Newtonmore in 1973 and a pair nesting near Nethy Bridge 1959 closely resembled this race.

Two-barred Crossbill *Loxia leucoptera*
(Vagrant)

Adult male found freshly dead Newtonmore 21st August 1959.

Common Crossbill *Loxia curvirostra*
(Visitor and undoubtedly breeds)

Influxes of continental Crossbills with smaller bills and shriller "chip-chip" calls, have been recognised during invasion years. Large invasions noted in 1909 and 1927. Noticeable influxes in July 1962 (85 Loch Garten 12th July); 1966 small numbers from 5th July; 1972 many from 26th June, maximum 150 Glenmore 22nd July, 120 Rothiemurchus 9th September. Small numbers in 1976, maximum 30 Rothiemurchus 8th September, not part of continental invasion. Big influx 1990–1, with 16 SW over Aviemore 18th June and 70 Tulloch 13th June 1990, more thereafter and a big return passage in May 1991, when total of about 800 in Abernethy Forest in mid May. Small numbers are difficult to separate from local birds except with good views; some probably stay for lengthy periods and may have even nested in district. Usually recorded in larches and spruces.

Scottish Crossbill *Loxia scotica*
(Numerous resident breeder, local movements)

One of the special birds of the old Caledonian pine forests and the only endemic bird species in the United Kingdom. Larger than previous species with distinctively larger bill adapted to deal with Scots Pine cones. Well distributed throughout pine forests of the valley, mainly in old native woods of Abernethy, Rothiemurchus and Dulnain. Numbers fluctuate and not known where birds go in poor years. Seventy to eighty pairs Rothiemurchus in good year of 1952, high numbers in 1962 and 1972; detailed studies at Loch Garten reserve showed good numbers in good cone year of 1978 (20–25 pairs nested), very few in 1979, none nesting in 1980 but pairs in 1981 bred with first reasonable cone crop since 1978.

142

Low numbers 1988 and very poor year 1989. Nest-building starts in winter (January 1978); young often fledge in May but eggs and young September 1983. Counts include 50 Glen Feshie 8th June 1960; 50 Loch Garten November–December 1977; 30 at tree line Lairig Ghru 27th June 1978 ; 60 Coylumbridge 22nd August 1987 and about 200 in Abernethy Forest survey mid May 1991. Will feed in larches in summer through to winter; flocks can often be located by looking for falling cones and recently opened cones on paths through pine forests.

Parrot Crossbill *Loxia pytyopsittacus*
(Rare visitor; has bred)

Two, probably six, Tulloch 11th April 1983. There was in invasion of Parrot Crossbills into Scotland and England in October 1982. Young male ringed Loch Garten 11th–22nd March 1987.
Skull found Abernethy 1988.
In May 1991, up to 10 seen Abernethy; pair with four young just out of nest at Loch Garten on 26th May; six seen in June elsewhere in forest and five in July.
Single birds trapped and ringed in Abernethy March and 4th October 1993.

Common Rosefinch *Carpodacus erythrinus*
(Rare summer visitor)

Single males reported in song Badenoch 27–28th June 1978, 7–27th June 1983 and 24th June 1983. Male singing near Kingussie 18th June 1987. Male singing near Laggan 6–7th June 1988, late May 1989 and 1st–14th June 1990. Immature Avielochan 4th September 1991 and one Aviemore 10th September 1992.

Bullfinch *Pyrrhula pyrrhula*
(Common resident breeder)

Nests throughout district in reasonable numbers, mainly in scrubby areas, thickets and dense plantations; elusive in breeding season. Gathers in foraging parties in autumn and winter and often moves up to highest tree limits to feed in long heather at up to 700 metres a.s.l.. Parties usually up to 10–12, maximum 43 Insh Marshes 11th January 1977. Numbers were high in winter 1976–7. Northern type birds suspected; for example, six Boat of Garten 15th January 1962 but not proved.

Hawfinch *Coccothraustes coccothraustes*
(Vagrant)

Five records of six birds:
Pair in Rothiemurchus April 1937.
One at the new bridge Grantown-on-Spey 6th–13th January 1985.
One Nethy Bridge 12–13th January 1993.
One Kincraig 9–10th July 1994.
Male Insh village 1–3rd December 1994.

Evening Grosbeak *Hesperiphona vespertina*
(Vagrant)

Adult female at a bird table in Nethy Bridge 10–25th March 1980.

Lapland Bunting *Calcarius lapponicus*
(Vagrant and has bred)

A male Creag Beag, Kingussie 23rd April 1968. In 1977, the year

of the amazing breeding influx in Scotland, at least one pair bred
in the mountains in this district with up to seven males and two
female observed in suitable nesting habitat. A single male in 1978
and one or two pairs with young and an extra male in 1979. All
the breeding groups in Scotland became extinct.

Snow Bunting *Plectrophenax nivalis*
(Rare breeder, numerous winter visitor)

Very small numbers have nested on the high mountains for
several centuries; numbers now as high as ever recorded but
annual fluctuations; some summers good success often with
double-broods.

Flocks of migrants occur in winter both on the low ground
and in the mountains; usually present in winter in ski car parks
on Cairngorm, 100 Cairngorm to Ben Macdhui December 1961,
200 Coire Cas 16th November 1988; 300 Carrbridge 21st March
1962, 50 on stubbles Tulloch 16th December 1962; also feeds

beside A9 trunk road Dalwhinnie to Drumochter, 100 Dalwhinnie 21st February 1971 and 120 feeding on barley spilt from lorry North Drumochter 13th February 1976. 120 Lochindorb 18th March 1989 and 120 Gaick 31st December 1989 but seems scarcer in winter around the farms in recent decades.

Yellowhammer *Emberiza citrinella*
(Scarce resident breeder)

Has decreased noticeably as a breeding species in the last 20 years, mainly due to changes in farming practices. Used to be six pairs on and around our croft in Tulloch in late 1970s, now down to one pair. Reported as rare at Insh from 1980, used to be up to 12 in a day in 1970s now single day records in 1983 and 1985, none since. Occurs in small numbers throughout district, mainly in agricultural and scrubby areas. Gathers in small flocks around farms in winter; maximum count 30 Inchdryne, Tulloch 13th March 1962, 40 on 27th December 1984 but only up to three or five in recent years.

Reed Bunting *Emberiza schoeniclus*
(Scarce resident breeder)

Nests in good numbers in Insh Marshes (20 pairs in 564 acres in 1977, 60 pairs in whole SSSI but fewer in recent years); also in marshy areas by rivers and lochs throughout district, also on drier bogs with bog myrtle and scrub, for example, two pairs Loch Morlich. Returns to nesting territories in early April; gathers in late summer in marshes and spends winter there and in agricultural lands. Maximum counts: 150 on stubbles Ruthven 11th December 1966, 60 Insh Marshes 2nd August 1980, 21 Tulloch 23rd December 1979. Recent counts lower; 12 Balavil

18th January 1987 and 12 Carrbridge 21st January 1990. Some may leave valley in winter.

Corn Bunting *Emberiza calandra*
(Extinct breeder and visitor)

Only recent records: Single males in song Dulnain Bridge May 1969 and Newtonmore June 1969; only seen once (Laggan) 1960–3. Probably used to breed in small numbers.

Finding Birds in Badenoch and Strathspey Checklist

People have different interests in observing birds. Some birders are adding to their life lists by coming to Strathspey, or may be adding several species to their year list. Other bird-watchers come to enjoy the birds and at the same time record of the numbers and different species at the the various sites and habitats they visit. Often they meticulously record this data and send them to local recorders, who produce annual bird reports. Records for Strathspey and Badenoch appear in the annual Highland Bird Report and a summary is sent for use in the Scottish Bird Report under the auspices of the Scottish Ornithologists' Club. The local recorder is: Colin Crooke, 8 George Street, Avoch, Ross-shire.

Many people holiday in the district and as part of their enjoyment of this beautiful place they take an interest in the birds, mammals, plants and other creatures they come across. And of course many local residents take a keen interest in their surroundings and it is my hope that this book helps all of these people.

Please remember that the welfare of the birds comes first and in Badenoch and Strathspey this is doubly important for many rare species breed here. It is important to remember that in an area with such high numbers of bird-watchers, it's the cumulative effects of nest visiting which can adversely affect breeding success; so please be careful.

Generally speaking, birds and animals are shy and will seek cover. Roads and paths through woodland and beside rivers will give the best chance of observing wildlife. Be as quiet as possible and it is worth stopping frequently at vantage points to listen for bird calls and to scan the surrounding area with binoculars.

Enjoy watching nesting birds but keep disturbance of them or their habitat to a minimum. Too close an approach will keep birds off their eggs and in cold or wet weather this will lead to the embryos being chilled or the eggs being deserted. Nest visiting can also help predators such as foxes and crows to locate nests and take the eggs or young.

Rare breeding birds on Schedule 1 of the Wildlife and Countryside Act are specially protected and it is illegal to wilfully disturb them at or near their nests, and this includes photography. If you do come across a rare bird's nest keep the information confidential, although it is useful to let the local recorder or conservation wardens know. Casual passing on of information may lead to the nests being robbed of their eggs.

It is very important to bear in mind the country code, especially to guard against fires which can be extraordinarily serious in spring and in dry periods. Leave gates as you find them and keep to paths through farm land. Firm control of dogs is important especially during the lambing season and when ground nesting birds have eggs and young. In many ways, it is wiser not to take dogs onto nature reserves. Also remember to respect the rights of people who live and work in the countryside. Bear in mind that deer stalking and grouse shooting take place from autumn into the winter. In many areas it's possible to telephone estate staff to get advice on the best routes into the mountains to avoid disturbance.

Be very careful when going into the mountains. Let someone know where you are going and when you intend to return, or leave a note in you car for the police in case you have an accident. Watch for changes in the weather, wear appropriate clothing and know how to use a map and compass.

The following checklist and bar graph gives every one an opportunity to keep track of what they have seen and also helps people new to the area work out the best time to see particular species. Readers should also use the species accounts, first and last dates and bird habitats, but the following inventory is a complete list of species which have occurred up to December 1994 in Badenoch and Strathspey.

Common means that the bird is easily seen in the district without any degree of difficulty as long as one visits the proper type of habitat and the length of the bar in the graph indicates the period in the year that the species is present. Remember that seasons can vary from year to year. Uncommon means that the species occurs in reasonable numbers in the proper type of habitat but often one needs time and effort to actually see the species. Rare means that the species is difficult to observe or occurs in very small numbers and that the chance of seeing this species in Badenoch and Strathspey may be unlikely.

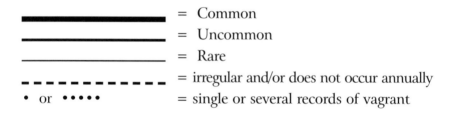

Species listed in bold capitals are regular breeding species in district e.g. GOOSANDER. A species in italic has bred in the region at some time in the past e.g. *Corncrake*. Non-breeding species are in plain type e.g. Great Snipe.

Three check list columns are provided, for example, they can be used for recording your personal list of species seen in the district, in your garden, from the house, on a particular reserve you visit, a year list etc.

Checklist A	
Checklist B	
Checklist C	

A	B	C	SPECIES	J	F	M	A	M	J	J	A	S	O	N	D
			RED-THROATED DIVER			▬	▬	▬	▬	▬	▬	▬		•	
			BLACK-THROATED DIVER				▬	▬	▬	▬	▬	▬			•
			Great Northern Diver		•				•	•		•			
			LITTLE GREBE	-	-	-	▬	▬	▬	▬	▬	▬	-	-	-
			Great Crested Grebe				••	••	•			•	•		
			Black-necked Grebe									•			
			SLAVONIAN GREBE				-	-	▬	▬					
			Fulmar		•				•••			•			
			Manx Shearwater							•	•••				
			Storm Petrel					•							•
			Leach's Petrel										-	-	
			Gannet		•			•		•		•			
			Cormorant	▬	▬	▬		-	-	-					
			Bittern	•											
			Little Bittern					•							
			GREY HERON	▬	▬	▬	▬	▬	▬	▬	▬	▬	▬	▬	▬
			White Stork					•							
			MUTE SWAN	▬	▬	▬	▬					▬	▬	▬	▬
			[Black Swan]				•								•
			Whooper Swan	▬	▬	▬	▬	-	-	-	-	-	▬	▬	▬
			Bean Goose			•									
			Pink-footed Goose				▬ ▬		•		•		▬ ▬ ▬ ▬		
			White-fronted Goose	•				- - -					- -		
			GREYLAG GOOSE	▬ ▬		▬	▬	▬	▬	▬	▬	▬	▬	▬	▬
			Snow Goose				•								
			Canada Goose		•	•		- - - -		•	- - - -			•	
			Barnacle Goose	▬•	••	•	•						- - - -		
			Brent Goose								• ▬		•		
			Red-breasted Goose			•									
			Shelduck		•	- - - -		- ▬	•	•	••	•	•	•	
			[Mandarin]				•	•					•		
			American Wigeon		•										
			WIGEON	▬	▬	▬	▬	▬	▬	▬	▬	▬	▬	▬	▬
			Gadwall				••	••					•		
			TEAL	▬	▬	▬	▬	▬	▬	▬	▬	▬	▬	▬	▬
			MALLARD	▬	▬	▬	▬	▬	▬	▬	▬	▬	▬	▬	▬
			Pintail	-	-	-	-	-	-	-	-	-	-	-	-
			Garganey				•	••	••	•					
			SHOVELER	-	-	▬	▬	▬	▬	▬	▬	-	-		
			Pochard	▬	▬	▬				▬	▬				

151

A	B	C	SPECIES	J	F	M	A	M	J	J	A	S	O	N	D
			Ring-necked Duck	••	••	••	••	••	••	••	••	••	••	••	••
			TUFTED DUCK	▬	▬	▬	▬	▬	▬	▬	▬	▬	▬	▬	▬
			Scaup	••	••	••		••		••	••	-	-	••	
			Long-tailed Duck				•	•					•••	••	••
			Scoter				•	•	•				•	•	••
			Surf Scoter									•			
			Velvet Scoter									•			
			GOLDENEYE	▬	▬	▬	▬	▬	▬	▬	▬	▬	▬	▬	▬
			Smew	••	••	••	••	••	••	••				•	••
			R. BREASTED MERGANSER	•		———	—	—	—	—	—	-	-	-	
			GOOSANDER	—	—	—	—	—	—	—	—	▬	▬		
			Ruddy Duck					•	•	•					
			Honey Buzzard					•	••	••	•••	•			
			Red Kite	••	••	••	•			•		••	••	••	••
			White-tailed Eagle	••		•	•			•		••	••	•	
			Marsh Harrier				-	-	-	-	-	-			
			HEN HARRIER	▬	▬	▬	▬	▬	▬	▬	▬	▬	▬	▬	▬
			Goshawk	-	-	-	-	-	-	-	-	-	-	-	-
			SPARROWHAWK	▬	▬	▬	▬	▬	▬	▬	▬	▬	▬	▬	▬
			BUZZARD	▬	▬	▬	▬	▬	▬	▬	▬	▬	▬	▬	▬
			Rough-legged Buzzard		•	••			•				•		
			GOLDEN EAGLE	▬	▬	▬	▬	▬	▬	▬	▬	▬	▬	▬	▬
			OSPREY			▬	▬	▬	▬	▬	▬		•		•
			KESTREL	▬	▬	▬	▬	▬	▬	▬	▬	▬	▬	▬	▬
			Red-footed Falcon					••	•						
			MERLIN	••	••	•	—	—	—	—	—	•	••	••	••
			Hobby					•	-	-	-	•			
			[Lanner Falcon]					•							
			[Saker Falcon]									•			
			GYR FALCON		•	••	•								
			PEREGRINE	▬	▬	▬	▬	▬	▬	▬	▬	▬	▬	▬	▬
			RED GROUSE	▬	▬	▬	▬	▬	▬	▬	▬	▬	▬	▬	▬
			PTARMIGAN	▬	▬	▬	▬	▬	▬	▬	▬	▬	▬	▬	▬
			BLACK GROUSE	▬	▬	▬	▬	▬	▬	▬	▬	▬	▬	▬	▬
			CAPERCAILLIE	▬	▬	▬	▬	▬	▬	▬	▬	▬	▬	▬	▬
			RED-LEGGED PARTRIDGE	▬	▬	▬	▬	▬	▬	▬	▬	▬	▬	▬	▬
			GREY PARTRIDGE	▬	▬	▬	▬	▬	▬	▬	▬	▬	▬	▬	▬
			Quail					•	••	••	••				
			[Reeve's Pheasant]												
			PHEASANT	▬	▬	▬	▬	▬	▬	▬	▬	▬	▬	▬	▬

A	B	C	SPECIES	J	F	M	A	M	J	J	A	S	O	N	D
			WATER RAIL			━	━	━	━	━	━			•	•
			SPOTTED CRAKE				┄	┄	┄	┄		•			
			Corncrake						•	•					
			MOORHEN	┅	┅	┅	━	━	━	━	━	┅	┅	┅	┅
			COOT	━	━	━	━	━	━	━	━	━	━	━	━
			Common Crane				••	•							
			OYSTERCATCHER	•	••	━	━	━	━	━	━	•	••	••	
			Avocet				•								
			RINGED PLOVER				━	━	━	━	━	•			
			DOTTEREL				•	━	━	━	━				
			GOLDEN PLOVER				━	━	━	━	━	━	•		
			LAPWING	•	••	━	━	━	━	━	━	┄	┄	┄	•
			Knot						•		•				
			Sanderling						•						
			Temminck's Stint					•	••	••					
			Purple Sandpiper					┄	┄	┄					
			DUNLIN	•				━	━	━	━		•	•	
			Ruff					•		•					
			Jack Snipe	•				•				•	••	••	••
			SNIPE	┄	┄	┄	━	━	━	━	━	┅	┅		
			Great Snipe							•	•				
			WOODCOCK	━	━	━	━	━							
			Black-tailed Godwit				┄	┄	┄						
			Bar-tailed Godwit				•	•		•					
			Whimbrel				┄	┄	┄	┄	┄				
			CURLEW	•		━	━	━	━	━	┄	┄	┄	••	•
			Spotted Redshank				••	•••		••					
			REDSHANK			━	━	━	━	━	┄		•		
			GREENSHANK				━	━	━	━	━	•	••		
			Green Sandpiper				•	••	••	••	••				
			WOOD SANDPIPER				━	━							
			COMMON SANDPIPER				••	━	━	━	••	•	•		
			Turnstone				•	•		•					
			Red-necked Phalarope					•	••	••					
			Pomarine Skua				•								
			Arctic Skua				•••				••		•		
			Long-tailed Skua						••						
			Great Skua			••					•				
			Little Gull				•								
			Sabine's Gull								•				

A	B	C	SPECIES	J	F	M	A	M	J	J	A	S	O	N	D
			BLACK-HEADED GULL	•	▬	▬	▬	▬	▬	▬	▬	-	-	-	•
			COMMON GULL		•	▬	▬	▬	▬	▬	▬	-	-	••	•
			Lesser Black-backed Gull	•		▬	▬	▬							
			HERRING GULL	▬	▬	▬	▬	▬	▬	▬	▬	▬	▬	▬	▬
			Iceland Gull	••	•	•	•								
			Glaucous Gull	••	•	••	•	•	•						
			GT BLACK-BACKED GULL	▬	▬	▬	▬	▬	▬	▬	▬	▬	▬	▬	▬
			Kittiwake	•	•	-	-	-		•			••	•	•
			Sandwich Tern						•	•					
			COMMON TERN					▬	▬	▬					
			Black Tern				•	•		•	•				
			Guillemot								••				
			Little Auk	••											
			Puffin				••		•						
			Pallas's Sand Grouse												
			[FERAL PIGEON]	▬	▬	▬	▬	▬	▬	▬	▬	▬	▬	▬	▬
			Stock Dove				-	-	-	-	-	-			•
			WOOD PIGEON	▬	▬	▬	▬	▬	▬	▬	▬	▬	▬	▬	▬
			COLLARED DOVE	▬	▬	▬	▬	▬	▬	▬	▬	▬	▬	▬	▬
			Turtle Dove					-	-	-		••			
			CUCKOO				••	▬	▬	▬	-	-	•		
			Barn Owl	-	-	-	-	-	-	-	-	-	-	-	-
			Snowy Owl				•	••	••	••	••	••	•	•	
			TAWNY OWL	▬	▬	▬	▬	▬	▬	▬	▬	▬	▬	▬	▬
			LONG-EARED OWL	▬	▬	▬	▬	▬	▬	▬	▬	▬	▬	▬	▬
			SHORT-EARED OWL				▬	▬	▬	▬	▬	▬	▬		
			Nightjar							••					
			SWIFT					▬	▬	▬	▬	••		•	
			Alpine Swift							•					
			KINGFISHER	▬	▬	▬	▬	▬	▬	▬	▬	▬	▬	▬	▬
			Roller												
			Hoopoe				••	•				••	•		
			Wryneck				-	-	-	-	-				
			GREEN WOODPECKER	▬	▬	▬	▬	▬	▬	▬	▬	▬	▬	▬	▬
			GT SPOTTED WOODPECKER	▬	▬	▬	▬	▬	▬	▬	▬	▬	▬	▬	▬
			SKYLARK	•	▬	▬	▬	▬	▬	▬	▬		••	•	
			Shorelark					•	••	••	••	•			
			SAND MARTIN				••	▬	▬	▬	▬	-	-		
			SWALLOW				•	▬	▬	▬	▬	▬	•		
			HOUSE MARTIN				•••	▬	▬	▬	▬	-	•		

154

A	B	C	SPECIES	J	F	M	A	M	J	J	A	S	O	N	D
			TREE PIPIT												
			MEADOW PIPIT												
			Yellow Wagtail												
			GREY WAGTAIL												
			PIED WAGTAIL												
			Waxwing												
			DIPPER												
			WREN												
			DUNNOCK												
			ROBIN												
			Bluethroat												
			Black Redstart												
			REDSTART												
			WHINCHAT												
			STONECHAT												
			WHEATEAR												
			RING OUZEL												
			BLACKBIRD												
			Fieldfare												
			SONG THRUSH												
			REDWING												
			MISTLE THRUSH												
			GRASSHOPPER WARBLER												
			SEDGE WARBLER												
			Marsh Warbler												
			Great Reed Warbler												
			Icterine Warbler												
			Lesser Whitethroat												
			WHITETHROAT												
			GARDEN WARBLER												
			BLACKCAP												
			WOOD WARBLER												
			Chiffchaff												
			WILLOW WARBLER												
			GOLDCREST												
			SPOTTED FLYCATCHER												
			PIED FLYCATCHER												
			LONG-TAILED TIT												
			Willow Tit												
			CRESTED TIT												

A	B	C	SPECIES	J	F	M	A	M	J	J	A	S	O	N	D
			COAL TIT	▬▬▬▬▬▬▬▬▬▬▬▬
			BLUE TIT	▬▬▬▬▬▬▬▬▬▬▬▬
			GREAT TIT	▬▬▬▬▬▬▬▬▬▬▬▬
			TREECREEPER	▬▬
			Golden Oriole					••	••						
			Red-backed Shrike					•	••	••	•	•			
			Great Grey Shrike	- - - - - - - - - -	-				- - - - - - - -
			Jay						•			••	•		
			MAGPIE	▬▬▬▬▬▬▬▬▬▬▬▬
			JACKDAW	▬▬▬▬▬▬▬▬▬▬▬▬
			ROOK	▬▬▬▬▬▬▬▬▬▬▬▬
			CARRION CROW	▬▬▬▬▬▬▬▬▬▬▬▬
			RAVEN	▬▬▬▬▬▬▬▬▬▬▬▬
			STARLING	▬▬▬▬▬▬▬▬▬▬▬▬
			HOUSE SPARROW	▬▬▬▬▬▬▬▬▬▬▬▬
			Tree Sparrow			•		••					•		
			CHAFFINCH	▬▬▬▬▬▬▬▬▬▬▬▬
			Brambling	▬ - - - - - - - - -	••		••	••			•	▬ ▬ ▬ ▬
			GREENFINCH	▬▬▬▬▬▬▬▬▬▬▬▬
			GOLDFINCH	▬▬▬▬▬▬▬▬▬▬▬▬
			SISKIN	▬ ▬▬
			LINNET	▬			▬▬▬▬▬▬	- - - - - - - -
			TWITE	▬▬▬▬▬▬▬▬▬▬▬▬
			REDPOLL	▬▬▬▬▬▬▬▬▬▬▬▬
			Two-barred Crossbill									•			
			COMMON CROSSBILL	- - - - - - - - - - - - - - - - - - -
			SCOTTISH CROSSBILL	▬▬▬▬▬▬▬▬▬▬▬▬
			Parrot Crossbill			•	•	••	••	••	••	•	•		
			Common Rosefinch					•	••			••			
			BULLFINCH	▬▬▬▬▬▬▬▬▬▬▬▬
			Hawfinch	••			•			•					•
			Evening Grosbeak			•									
			Lapland Bunting				•	•••	••	•					
			SNOW BUNTING	▬▬▬▬▬▬▬▬▬▬▬▬
			YELLOWHAMMER	▬▬▬▬▬▬▬▬▬▬▬▬
			REED BUNTING	▬▬▬▬▬▬▬▬▬▬▬▬
			Corn Bunting					•	•						

Selected Bibliography

Baxter, E. V. and Rintoul, L. J. *The Birds of Scotland*, Oliver & Boyd, Edinburgh 1953

Brown, P. and Waterston, G. *The Return of the Osprey*, Collins, London, 1962

Buckland, S. T., Bell, M.V. and Picozzi, N. *The Birds of North-East Scotland*, Aberdeen University Press, Aberdeen, 1990

Cook, M. *The Birds of Moray and Nairn*, Mercat Press, Edinburgh, 1992

Darling, F. F. & Boyd, J. M. *The Highlands and Islands*, Collins, London, 1969

Dennis, R. *Birds of Badenoch & Strathspey*, Roy Dennis, Inverness, 1984

Dennis, R. *Ospreys*, Colin Baxter Photography Ltd, Lanark, 1991

Dennis, R. *Peregrine Falcons*, Colin Baxter Photography Ltd, Lanark, 1991

Dennis, R. *Divers*, Colin Baxter Photography Ltd, Grantown-on-Spey, 1993

Gibbons, D. W., Reid, J.B. & Chapman, R. A. *The New Atlas of Breeding Birds in Britain and Ireland: 1988–1991*, Poyser, Calton, 1993

Gordon, S. *The Hill Birds of Scotland*, Edward Arnold, London, 1915

Gordon, S. *The Cairngorm Hills of Scotland*, Cassell, London, 1925

Gordon, S. *The Golden Eagle*, Collins, London, 1955

Harvie-Brown, J. A. & Buckley, T. E. *A Vertebrate Fauna of the Moray Basin.* (2 Volumes), David Douglas, Edinburgh, 1895

Jenkins, D. *Land Use in the River Spey Catchment*, ITE, Huntingdon, 1988

Lack, P. *The Atlas of Wintering Birds in Britain and Ireland*, Poyser, Calton, 1986

Nethersole-Thompson, D. *The Greenshank*, Collins, London, 1951

Nethersole-Thompson, D. *The Snow Bunting*, Oliver & Boyd, Edinburgh, 1966

Nethersole-Thompson, D. *The Dotterel*, Collins London, 1973

Nethersole-Thompson, D. *Pine Crossbills*, Poyser, Berkhamstead, 1974

Nethersole-Thompson, D. and Watson, A. *The Cairngorms*, Melvens, Perth, 1981

Thom. V. *Birds in Scotland*, Poyser, Calton, 1986

Waterston, G. *Ospreys in Speyside*, RSPB, Sandy, 1971

Webster, M. M. *Flora of Moray, Nairn and East Inverness*, Aberdeen University Press, Aberdeen, 1978

Individual references in the following ornithological journals :
Bird Study
British Birds (especially older volumes)
Ibis (mainly older volumes)
Scottish Birds (including Bird Reports)
Scottish Naturalist

Annual reports and other data from the RSPB reserves at Insh Marshes and Abernethy.

Index